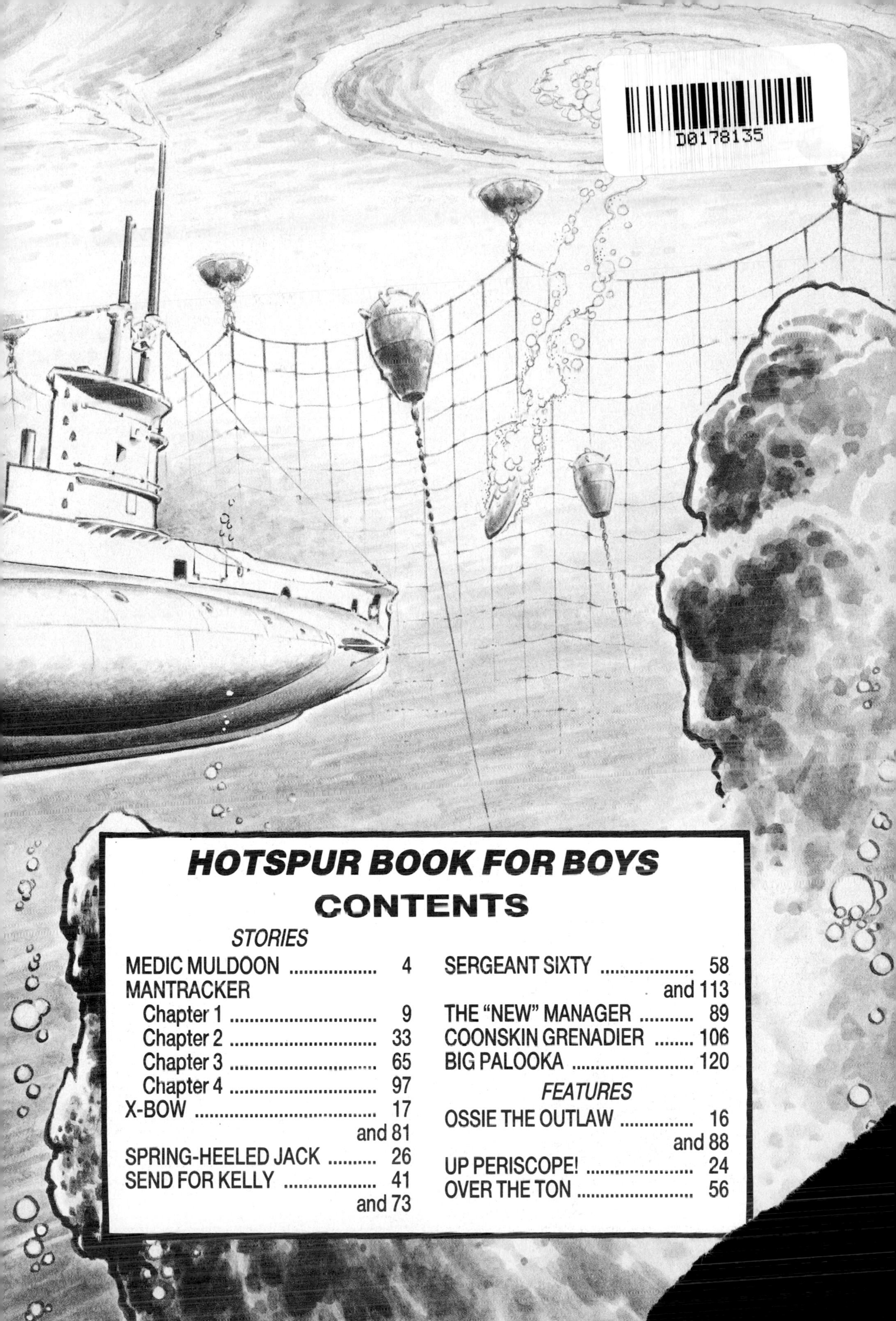
D0178135

HOTSPUR BOOK FOR BOYS

CONTENTS

STORIES

FEATURES

MEDIC MULDOON

CEASE FIRING!
MAY AS WELL STROLL DOWN AND SEE WHAT WE'VE BAGGED, MULDOON!

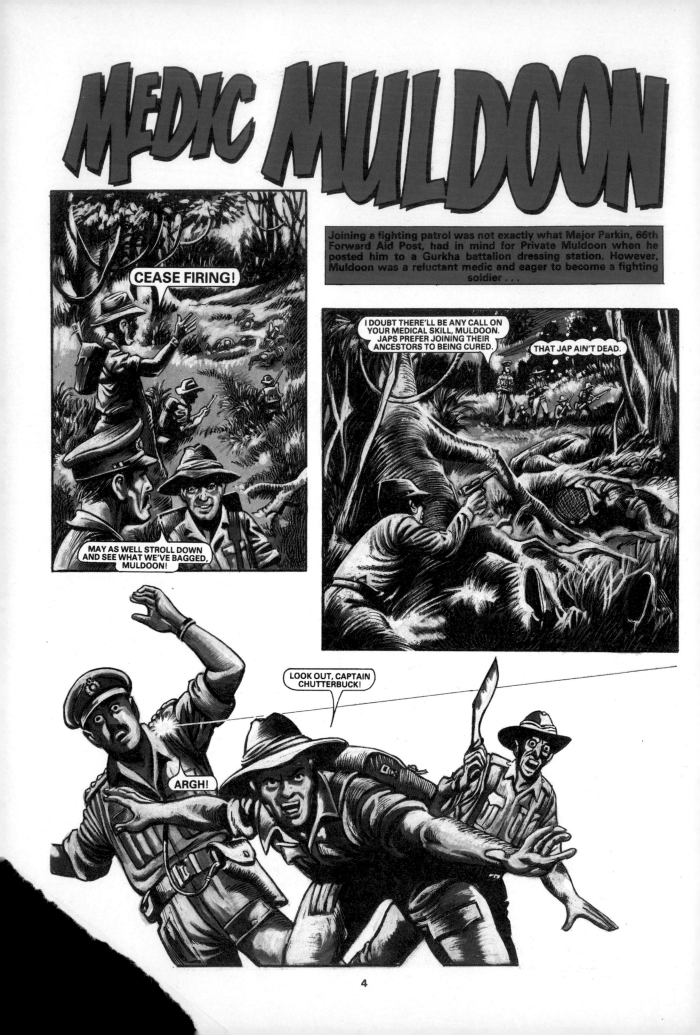

Joining a fighting patrol was not exactly what Major Parkin, 66th Forward Aid Post, had in mind for Private Muldoon when he posted him to a Gurkha battalion dressing station. However, Muldoon was a reluctant medic and eager to become a fighting soldier . . .

I DOUBT THERE'LL BE ANY CALL ON YOUR MEDICAL SKILL, MULDOON. JAPS PREFER JOINING THEIR ANCESTORS TO BEING CURED.
THAT JAP AIN'T DEAD.

LOOK OUT, CAPTAIN CHUTTERBUCK!
ARGH!

JUST A BUSTED CLAVICLE, SIR. YOU'VE WON A TRIP BACK TO INDIA.
WHICH IS BETTER THAN WHERE I'D BE GOING IF YOU HADN'T GIVEN ME THAT JOG. MY THANKS, MULDOON.

When they returned to base . . .
BLIMEY, MAJOR PARKIN'S TURNED UP!

YOU SENT US A GOOD MAN IN MULDOON, SIR! HE'S ALWAYS EAGER TO BE WHERE THE ACTION IS.
HUM! TOO BAD YOU'LL BE LOSING HIM NOW I HAVE BROUGHT UP A REGULAR ORDERLY FOR THIS DRESSING STATION.

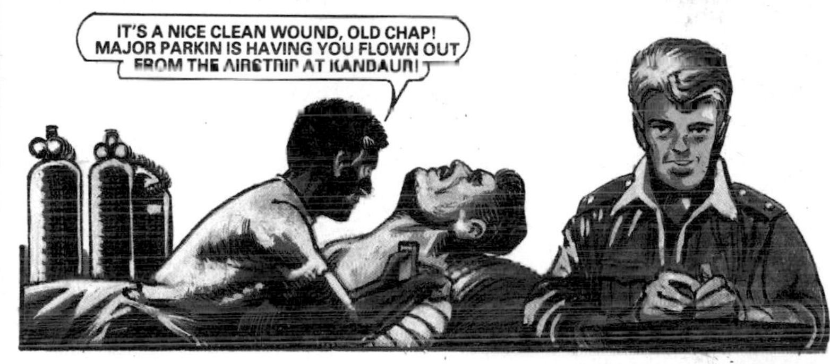
IT'S A NICE CLEAN WOUND, OLD CHAP! MAJOR PARKIN IS HAVING YOU FLOWN OUT FROM THE AIRSTRIP AT KANDAUR!

MULDOON, CAN YOU THINK OF A QUIET PLACE FOR A MEDICAL DISCUSSION?
HUH — ER, BEHIND THE FIELD KITCHEN, SIR.

Major Parkin had his own way of lecturing . . .
MULDOON, THEE'S A POINT YOU NEED TO REMEMBER . . .

THE DUTY OF A MEDICAL ORDERLY IS NOT TO INDULGE IN MILITARY BRAVADO, BUT TO ATTEND TO THE CASUALTIES OF WAR . . . AND IT PAINS ME TO HAVE TO KEEP IMPRESSING THIS FACT ON YOU.
YESSIR! IT PAINS ME TOO, SIR!

Captain Chutterbuck travelled back with Parkin and Muldoon. On the road . . .
THAT LOOKS LIKE A NAGA HILLMAN, BUT IT COULD BE A JAP TRICK. WE'VE HAD REPORTS OF INFILTRATION BY SMALL SUICIDE SQUADS OF 'EM.
THERE IS ONLY ONE WAY TO FIND OUT, CHUTTERBUCK!

HULLOA! JOLLY NICE DAY, EH, WHAT! I STOP YOU. TELL YOU JAPONI UP ON HILL.
INFILTRATION SQUAD! I'D BEST SEE WHAT THEY ARE UP TO — IF THIS NATIVE GENTLEMAN WILL BE SO GOOD AS TO GUIDE ME.

Half-a-mile on . . .
NO NEED FOR YOU TO COME TOO, MULDOON.
I'D BETTER, SIR. REMEMBER WHAT YOU SAID ABOUT WATCHING YOU AND LEARNING.
CHARLIE HEAR SOMETHING.

BANZAI!
LUMME JAPS!

GRAB HOLD OF THIS!

STONE THE CROWS!
THAT FELLOW VERY GOOD.

WE'VE SEEN JAPS, SIR! HOW ABOUT TAKING THE CAPTAIN'S ADVICE AND HEADING BACK TO BATTALION?
NOT TILL I AM MORE SURE OF THE SITUATION! KINDLY TIE UP THESE TWO PERSONS AND WE SHALL PROCEED.

THOSE TWO MUST HAVE COME ON RECCE AFTER OUR JEEP WAS SPOTTED. CHARLIE SAYS THERE ARE A LOT MORE!
NO SLUR ON THIS GENTLEMAN INTENDED, BUT I PREFER TO SEE FOR MYSELF, MULDOON.

HUM — ER, YES. I WOULD SAY THOSE ARE JAPANESE SOLDIERS UP THERE. WE MUST GET CLOSER TO SEE WHAT THEY'RE UP TO!

Charlie led them above the Jap position . . .
TWO MORTARS AND A MACHINE-GUN!
WHY DOES THAT OFFICER KEEP SCANNING THE ROAD?

THERE'S THE REASON — A MOTOR CONVOY!

WE GOT TO TRY AND WARN THOSE TRUCKS BEFORE THEY GET CHOPPED.
WE CAN DO BETTER THAN THAT.

PUT YOUR BACKS INTO IT! ALL TOGETHER — HEAVE!

IT'S GOING — IT'S GONE!

IT'S STARTED AN AVALANCHE!
THAT'S JUST WHAT I HOPED, MULDOON!

HUM — ER, I WOULD SAY THAT CONVOY IS NOW SAFE!
YESSIR! YOU COULD SAY THAT.

Charlie simply vanished, then Parkin and Muldoon moved on with the jeep . . .
WE HALTED THE CONVOY! THERE SEEMED TO BE A BIT OF COMMOTION AHEAD, SIR.
ALL OVER NOW, OLD CHAP — BUT THERE ARE A COUPLE OF TIED-UP JAPS YOU CAN TAKE INTO CARE.

At Kandaw . . .
I DID WANT TO SAY CHEERIO TO MAJOR PARKIN AND PRIVATE MULDOON.
THEY'RE BUSY, CAPTAIN CHUTTERBUCK! ONE OF THEIR LITTLE — ER, DISCUSSIONS!

MULDOON. I HAVE AGREED TO YOUR REQUEST FOR THIS MEETING, BUT I FAIL TO SEE THE POINT OF IT.
SIR, THE POINT IS TO REMIND YOU ABOUT WHAT YOU KEEP TELLING ME ABOUT US MEDICS NOT GOING IN FOR MILITARY BRAVADO.

SO I'M REMINDING YOU, SIR — WITH RESPECT.
EURGH!

SIR, IT REALLY PAINED ME TO HAVE TO DO THAT.
MULDOON, KINDLY SHUT UP.
THE END

MANTRACKER

Bearpaw Jay, ex-Vietnam war veteran and Indian warrior, had turned bounty hunter and become the most feared mantracker in the United States.

CHAPTER 1 KIDNAP!

WHAT ARE YOU GUYS WAITING FOR? THERE'S A TON OF PURE WHITE HEROIN IN THAT STORE.
SURE, DON JOSE. WE GO SEE.
WHICH IS EXACTLY THE WAY I PLANNED IT . . .
MEX LUGHEADS! IF THEY DON'T HURRY, I COULD LOSE TEN MILLION BUCKS IN DOPE.
BUSTER, YOU GOT A CHOICE. BEHAVE OR BE DEAD.
URHH — EASY . . . GO EASY!
KLEIST! YOU KILLED HIM?
LAWYERS AREN'T MY GAME. HE'LL JUST WAKE WITH A STIFF NECK — BUT YOU COULD END UP STIFF ALL OVER IF YOU DON'T CO-OPERATE!
DON JOSE, EEZ THAT YOU?
HELP ME! THIS CRAZY MAN'S GOT A GUN ON ME.
THAT IS NOT WHAT I CALL CO-OPERATING!
HEY — WHAT . . .
I WISH YOU HADN'T DONE THAT.
NOW IT'S GOING TO BE NOISY GETTIN' OUTA HERE!
SCREEEEEEECH!

ARGH! ARE YOU TRYING TO KILL US?
CRASH!
I THINK WE'LL TAKE SOME OF THESE HORSES ALONG WITH US!
RATA TAT TAT!
At the village of the ranch workers where a road block was being set up . . .
SI, SI! WE ARE READY.
ESCUCHE! SOMETHING COMES!
ANSWER ME! WHAT IS GOING ON?

THANKS, HORSES — YOU CLEARED THE WAY NICELY!
I'D BE OBLIGED IF YOU'D ASK YOUR BOYS ON THE MAIN GATE TO OPEN UP AND SAVE ME TRYING TO SMASH THROUGH.
THAT GATE'S TOO STRONG TO SMASH! ONLY YOU'RE CRAZY ENOUGH TO TRY . . . AND KILL US BOTH IN THE PROCESS!
DON JOSE ON RADIO! HE SAY TO OPEN THE GATES.
WE BETTER DO IT. HE EEZ THE BOSS.
YOU MADE THE RIGHT CHOICE THERE, BUSTER.
BLAST YOU!
INJUN, YOU AIN'T FOOLED MY BOYS BY HEADING SOUTH NOT NORTH. THAT'LL BE THEM BEHIND US!
YUP! RECKON YOU ARE RIGHT . . . BUT THEN I EXPECTED AS MUCH!
I'VE MADE PREPARATIONS! THIS'LL FIX THEM!

R-RR-RRUMBLE!
LOOK OUT — ARGHHHH!
THAT SEEMS TO HAVE SLOWED 'EM UP A MITE!
THAT STRINGBAG! AW NO, YOU CAN'T FLY ME OUT IN AN OLD WRECK LIKE THAT!
LIGHT UP THE FLARES, AMIGO.
SI, SENOR!
I'M TAKING OFF THE BRACELETS SO'S YOU CAN SIGN A QUIT-CLAIM SAYING YOU ARE COMING ALONG WILLINGLY. KEEPS THE RECORD STRAIGHT!
WHY NOT? I KNOW WHEN I'M BEAT!
ONLY I AIN'T BEAT YET, INJUN!
ANOTHER WRONG DECISION, BUSTER!

HERE'S WHERE YOU FEED ON YOUR OWN POISON! IT SHOULD PROVE FATAL!
NO, NOT THAT — PLEASE! I'LL SIGN.

With the form signed, Jay took off . . .

INJUN, YOU'RE SO SMART — BUT YOU'RE A DEAD MAN! MY BOYS'LL GET YOU WHEREVER YOU TRY TO HIDE!
The Gazzet
INDIAN SLEUTH
NABS CRIME BOS

Jay collected his reward then flew back to the reservation to the home of an old friend, Teeler Featherfoot — junk merchant and millionaire!

THERE'S THE HELICOPTER I WAS TELLING YOU ABOUT! I'LL GIVE YOU A GOOD TRADE-IN ON YOUR OL' BIPLANE.
FORD

I'LL THINK ABOUT IT. RIGHT NOW I AIM TO VACATION AND MAYBE TAKE MY TURN AT HERDING THE TRIBE'S CATTLE.

Attorney Kleist visited his client . . .

JOE, I'M PULLING STRINGS, BUT YOU BROKE BAIL ONCE AND I DOUBT THERE'S ANY LEGAL WAY TO GET YOU SPRUNG.
SO FIND AN ILLEGAL WAY — JUST GET ME OUT! THERE'S ANOTHER CHORE NEEDING DOING . . .
I WANT THAT CRAZY INJUN DEAD!

CONTINUED ON PAGE 33

OSSIE the OUTLAW

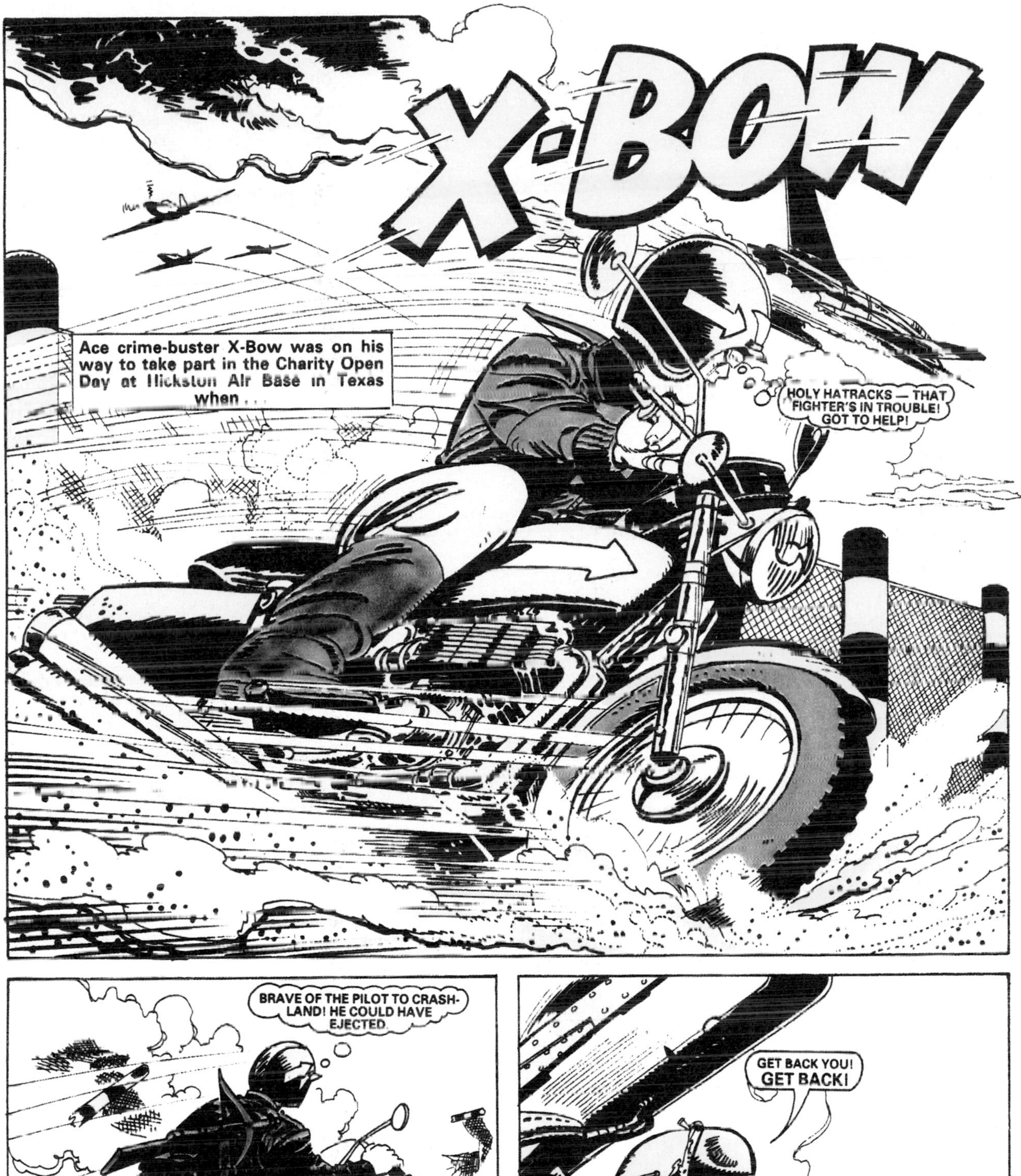

X-BOW

Ace crime-buster X-Bow was on his way to take part in the Charity Open Day at Hickston Air Base in Texas when . . .

HOLY HATRACKS — THAT FIGHTER'S IN TROUBLE! GOT TO HELP!

AAAAAH!
NOBODY IS GONNA TOUCH THIS PLANE!

GOT TO LOOSEN THE NOSE CONE BEFORE ANYBODY . . .
PHEW. BULLET MUST'VE HIT MY HELMET AND STUNNED ME!

THE POOR GUY'S BEEN KNOCKED STUPID. PROBABLY THINKS HE'S DOWN IN ENEMY TERRITORY.

BETTER TRANQUILLISE HIM BEFORE HE TAKES IT INTO HIS HEAD TO DESTROY SEVERAL MILLION DOLLARS WORTH OF AIRFORCE PROPERTY!
UNNNNNGH!

X-Bow radioed the exact location of the crash and soon . . .
THANKS, X-BOW. WE'LL PUT A GUARD ON HER TILL SHE CAN BE MOVED.
GREAT. I'LL HEAD ON TO THE AIR SHOW.

OPEN DAY
MILITARY PERSONNEL AND PERFORMERS ONLY
WELCOME, X-BOW! MAKE FOR AREA Z-2.
THANKS!
MP

X-Bow took a short-cut but—
YOU'RE OFF LIMITS, BUD! THIS IS MAH TERRITORAH. YOU GOT TO GO ALL THE WAY ROUND.
SORRY, BUT I'M A BIT LATE!

MUSTN'T MISS MY SLOT, SERGEANT!
WHY YOU . . .?
I'LL BREAK YOH IN HALF NEXT TIME AH SEE YOH — OR MY NAME AIN'T ELMER JOHNSON!
JUMPED-UP SO-AND-SO!
JUST IN TIME! HERE COME THE GUYS I'M TEAMED UP WITH!
X-BOW'S MADE IT, DAD!
WOW!
BRAVO! BRILLIANT! WHAT A MACHINE!

Meanwhile, at the crashed fighter . . .
WHAT DO THESE CHOPPERS WANT? MUST HAVE LOST THEIR WAY!

HA-HA, LOOK AT 'EM! HEY, THE AIR DISPLAY'S THAT A-WAY!

AAAAANGH! AIEEEEE!
THAT'S TAKEN CARE OF THEM! GET THE NOSE-CONE!

Back at Hickston Field . . .
COME QUICKLY, X-BOW! AN EMERGENCY!
RIGHT AWAY, COLONEL HAY!

THE GUARDS HAVE BEEN KILLED AND VITAL RADAR EQUIPMENT HAS BEEN TAKEN!

THERE ARE NO SURVIVORS, SIR — BUT WE FOUND THIS!
A RUSSIAN COIN, EH? SOMEBODY MADE A FOOLISH MISTAKE.

THAT PLANE WAS RETURNING FROM ONE OF OUR REGULAR TRAINING FLIGHTS TO THE CARIBBEAN, WHERE WE TEST SOME OF OUR MOST ADVANCED ELECTRONICS. THAT'S WHAT THE RUSSIANS WILL BE AFTER!

That night in nearby Houston . . .
THE F.B.I. WANT ME TO CHECK OUT THAT RUSKIE TRADE MISSION BUILDING — BUT IT'S A WILD GOOSE CHASE!

BEEP! BEEP!
MY TRANSMITTER DOWN THERE WILL DE-ACTIVATE THE ELECTRONIC ALARMS.

THROUGH HERE NOW.
SO, A VISITOR . . . JUST AS WELL I WORKED LATE.

UUUUURGH!

WHAT A FOOL YOU ARE, X-BOW! AS IF WE'D HAVE ATTEMPTED SUCH A THING ON AMERICAN SOIL!
I TRIED TO TELL THE F.B.I. THAT! THEY COULD HAVE STARTED A WAR. YOU ARE . . .?

GREGOR LUBYAKI, HEAD OF THE RUSSIAN TRADE MISSION. NO, MY FRIEND, SOME OTHER POWER DID THE DEED AND TRIED TO FRAME US.
IT'S POSSIBLE.

BELIEVE ME, WE ARE AS ANXIOUS TO UNMASK THE CULPRITS AS YOU ARE. WE SHALL BE WORKING ON IT. NOW GO!
WELL, GOOD LUCK ANY WAY.

X-Bow had to begin again! He gained entry to other embassies and trade missions — but to no avail!

X-Bow headed for F.B.I. headquarters to report . . .
NOT A TRACE OF ANYTHING! I — JEEPERS, THAT LITTLE BOY! THAT CAR CAN'T STOP IN TIME!

PHEW!
MY BALL!

MANIAC! I'M GONNA HAVE A WORD WITH HIM!
W . . . WOW! IT'S X-BOW!

HE WON'T GET AWAY!

STREWTH! THE CAR'S BLOWN UP!

CONTINUED ON PAGE 81

UP

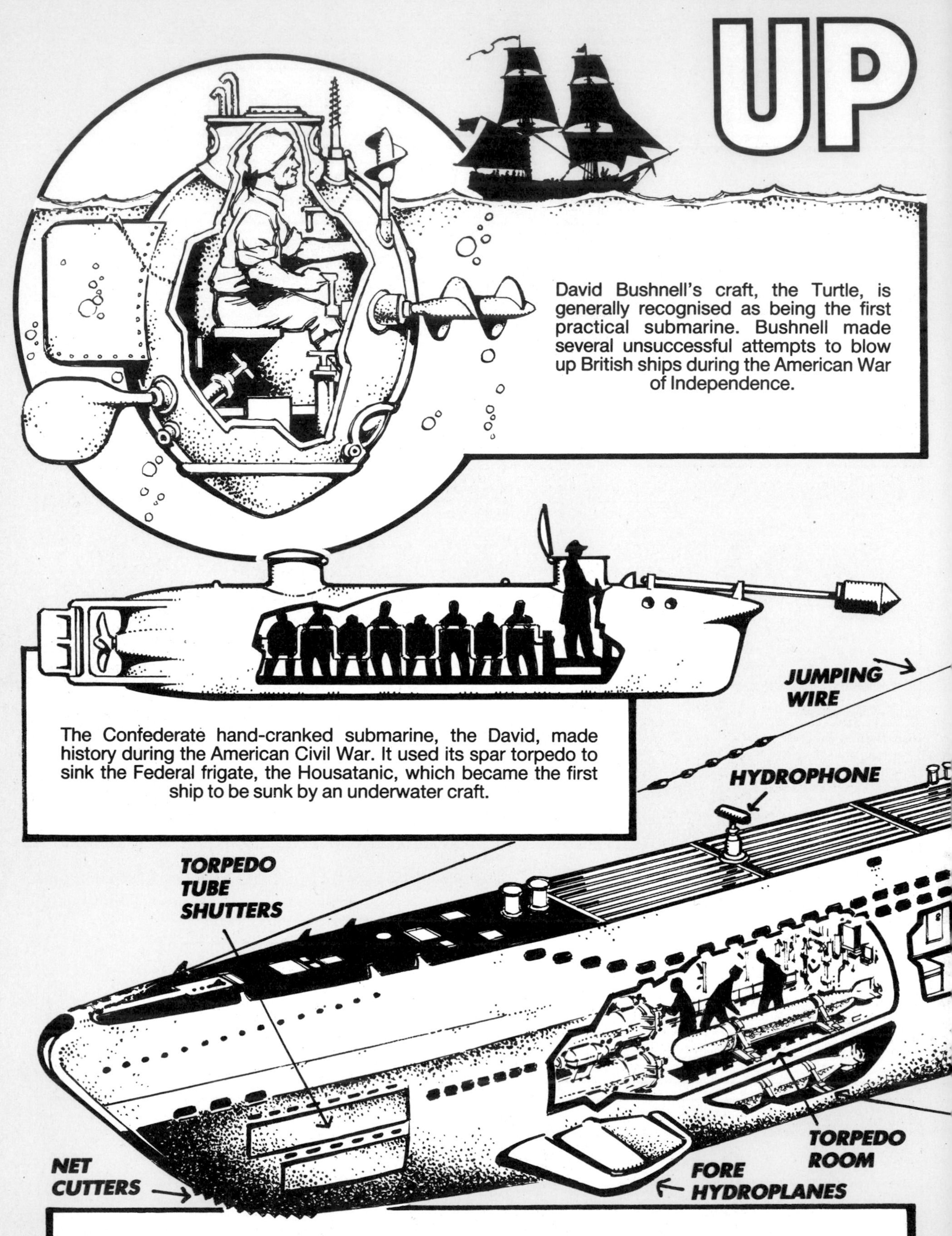

David Bushnell's craft, the Turtle, is generally recognised as being the first practical submarine. Bushnell made several unsuccessful attempts to blow up British ships during the American War of Independence.

The Confederate hand-cranked submarine, the David, made history during the American Civil War. It used its spar torpedo to sink the Federal frigate, the Housatanic, which became the first ship to be sunk by an underwater craft.

During the Second World War, Germany pinned her hopes of victory at sea on her U-boat fleet. The most famous design was the Type V11, Atlantic, of which over 700 were built. They had a surface speed of 18 knots, an underwater speed of 8 knots and carried 12 torpedoes.

PERISCOPE!

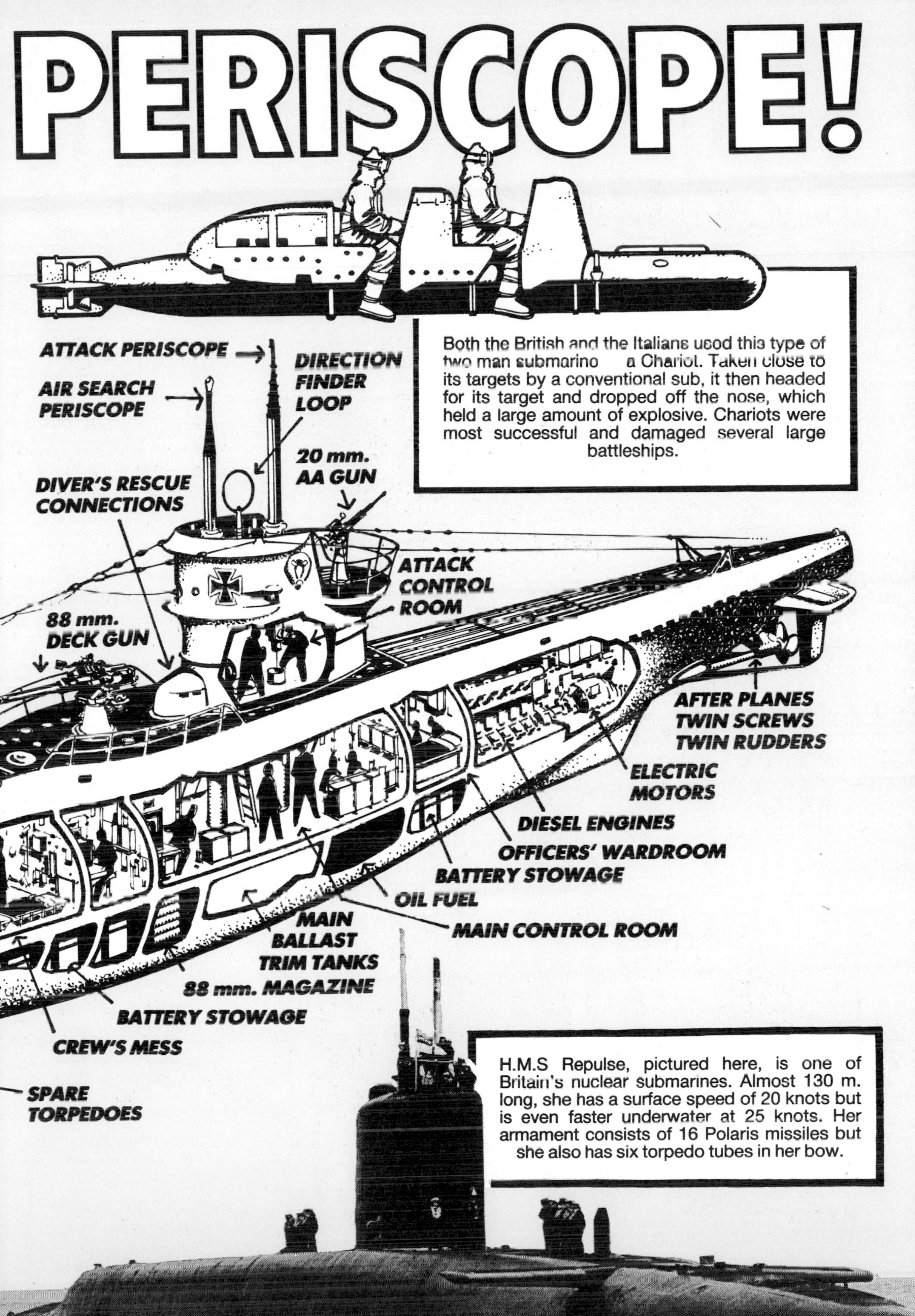

Both the British and the Italians used this type of two man submarine a Chariot. Taken close to its targets by a conventional sub, it then headed for its target and dropped off the nose, which held a large amount of explosive. Chariots were most successful and damaged several large battleships.

H.M.S Repulse, pictured here, is one of Britain's nuclear submarines. Almost 130 m. long, she has a surface speed of 20 knots but is even faster underwater at 25 knots. Her armament consists of 16 Polaris missiles but she also has six torpedo tubes in her bow.

SPRING-HEELED JACK

John Johnson was a quiet mild-mannered clerk at Ravell Row police station in Victorian London. One day he visited a prison hulk on the Thames with Sergeant Drew . . .

I'LL GET YOU, DREW, ONE DAY, FOR PUTTING ME AWAY!

OH DEAR, WHAT A VIOLENT MAN!

YOU 'ORRIBLE PIECE OF TRASH, MALONE. YOU'LL BE AN OLD MAN WHEN YOU GETS OUT O' HERE. YOU'LL HARDLY BE FIT TO LIGHT YOUR PIPE!

Unknown to anyone, John Johnson was also Spring-Heeled Jack, deadly enemy of the underworld!

I'LL NEED THESE BARGES! THERE AREN'T ENOUGH RESCUE BOATS.

IT'S SPRING-HEELD JACK!
HE PUTS LOTS OF US AWAY — BUT HE'S COMIN' TO RESCUE US!

BLESS EE, JACK!
GET THEM ABOARD, QUICKLY!

Jack saved most of the prisoners but some had perished before he arrived!
GOODBYE, I COULD DO NO MORE!
YOU DID WELL, JACK! GOODBYE!

Next day . . .
BRAVE CHAP, THAT SPRING-HEELED JACK, RISKING HIS NECK FOR A BUNCH OF CUT-THROATS! BY THE WAY, THAT'S A LIST OF THEM 'AS PERISHED. OUR FRIEND PUG MALONE'S AMONGST 'EM! I'D SAY HE GOT HIS JUST DESSERTS!

TAKE THESE 'ERE PAPERS TO JUDGE HALBERT'S CHAMBERS. HE'LL BE WORKING LATE.
VERY GOOD, SERGEANT DREW.

THE JUDGE'S CHAMBERS ARE UP HERE — I SAY!

UUUUURFFFFF!
NOT A HINT OF AN APOLOGY — BUT WHAT A STRANGE MARK ON HIS WRIST.

JUDGE HALBERT? IT'S ME! THE MESSENGER FROM RAVELL ROW!

GOODNESS!

HE'S BEEN CLUBBED TO DEATH.

Sergeant Drew was soon on the scene . . .
THIS FIGURE YOU SAW, JACKSON. DID YOU NOTICE ANYTHING SIGNIFICANT ABOUT HIM?
YES, AN ANGRY RED WEAL ON HIS RIGHT WRIST.

HMMM . . . THAT'LL HELP. IF ONLY YOU'D SEEN HIS FACE, THOUGH.

I'M SORRY!

The following day as Myles Mortimer, a famous lawyer, was making his way home . . .
SPARE A COPPER, SIR.
WHY CERTAINLY, OLD FELLOW!

AAAAAH!
I'LL 'AVE ALL YER MONEY!

Next morning . . .
FOOTPADS RIFE AGAIN, JACKSON. MYLES MORTIMER WAS STRUCK DOWN LAST NIGHT AND HIS WALLET TAKEN.
MYLES MORTIMER? FOOTPADS? IT COULDN'T BE THE SAME CHAP THAT KILLED JUDGE HALBERT, COULD IT?

CERTAINLY NOT, JACKSON. YOU STICK TO YOUR PEN PUSHING . . . I'LL DO THE DETECTIVE WORK.
BUT I THINK IT WAS . . . AND I KNOW WHERE HE'LL STRIKE NEXT!

That night . . .
SERGEANT DREW'S TAKING HIS SON TO THE CIRCUS.

I'LL KEEP THEM IN SIGHT!
WESTMINSTER
GREENWICH DEPTFORD OLD KENT ROAD
773
WICH
ROAD

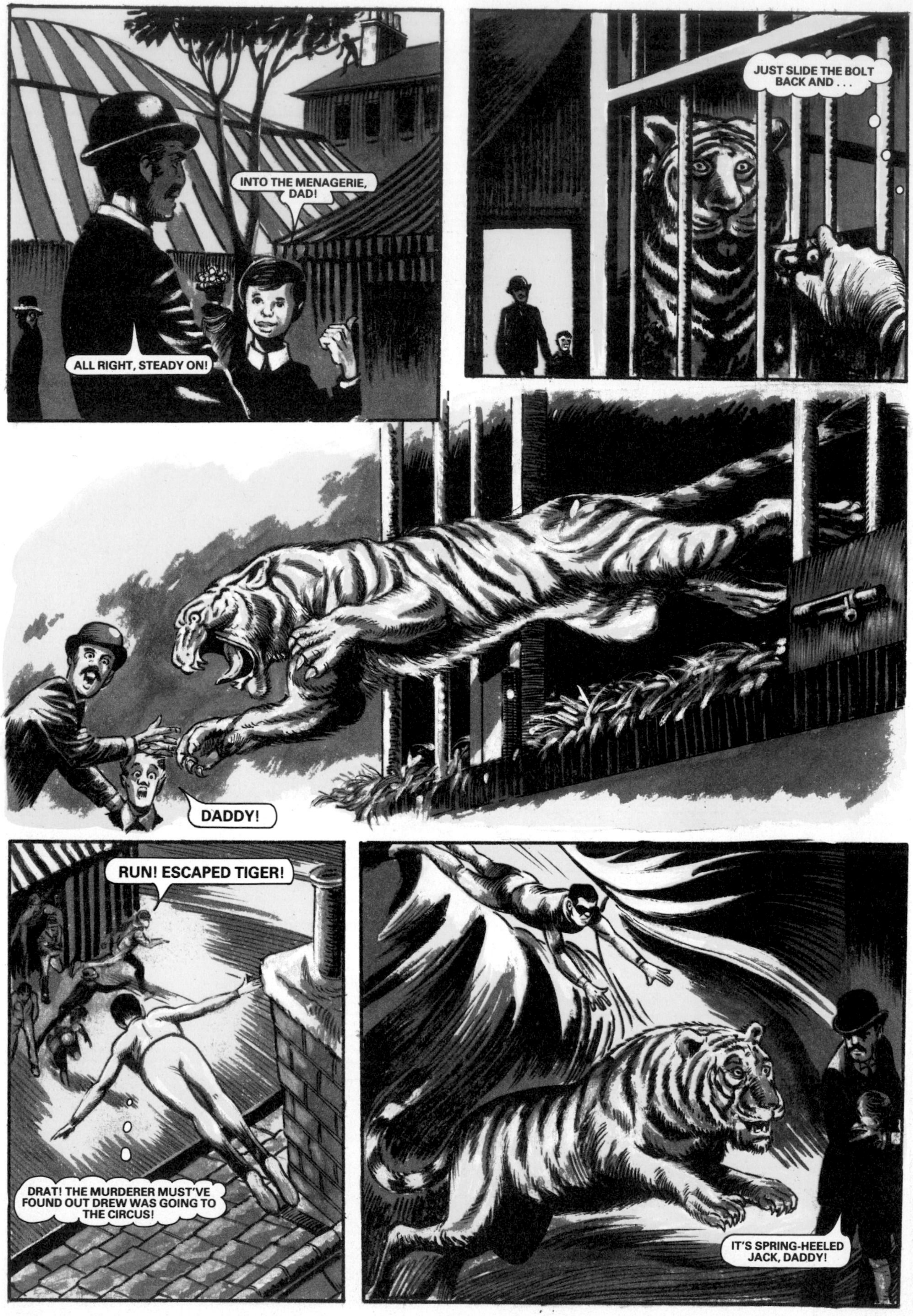

INTO THE MENAGERIE, DAD!

ALL RIGHT, STEADY ON!

JUST SLIDE THE BOLT BACK AND . . .

DADDY!

LEAVE HIM TO ME!

THERE'S NO TIME TO BE GENTLE!

POOR CREATURE! BUT THAT'S THE ONLY WAY!

The tiger quickly recognised who was master . . .
THERE'S A NICE PUSSYCAT — BACK INTO YOUR CAGE WITH YOU.

THANK YOU, JACK. I'LL COMPLAIN TO THE CIRCUS PEOPLE. DOWNRIGHT CARELESSNESS, THAT WAS.
I'LL HAVE A QUICK LOOK AROUND. BUT I THINK OUR MAN WILL BE LYING LOW AT THE MOMENT.

Jack was right! There was no sign of the would-be murderer! Later . . .
IT WAS A MARVELLOUS CIRCUS, DADDY! IT WAS REALLY EXCITING SEEING SPRING-HEELED JACK.
I'VE BEEN WATCHING FROM A DISTANCE ALL EVENING. NOW I THINK IT'S TIME I JOINED THEM AGAIN.

WHAT THE . . . ?
DON'T PANIC, PEOPLE. MAY I CHECK YOUR TICKETS, PLEASE?

PAH . . . ALL RIGHT, NUISANCE!
THANK YOU, SIR!

AAAAAH!
I THOUGHT IT WAS YOU, MALONE! FALSE BEARD WITH SOME STOLEN CLOTHES . . .

. . . BUT THE MANACLE MARK ON YOUR WRIST GAVE YOU AWAY. YOU GOT YOUR REVENGE ON THE JUDGE AND THE PROSECUTING LAWYER WHO SENT YOU TO PRISON — SERGEANT DREW WAS THE LAST ON YOUR DEATH LIST!
G . . . GOODNESS! THANK YOU, JACK.

Next day . . .
MALONE STARTED THE FIRE HIMSELF, DURING HIS ESCAPE! HE HOPED ALL THE PRISONERS WOULD PERISH AND WE'D THINK HE WAS DEAD. AS IT HAPPENED, WE DID THINK THAT! WHAT PUT SPRING-HEELED JACK ON TO HIM, I WONDER?
MAYBE HE LINKED THE TWO MURDERS, LIKE ME . . .

YOU KEEP YOUR REMARKS TO YOURSELF, JACKSON. YOU KNOW NOTHING OF SLEUTHING AND DETECTIVE WORK.
S . . . SORRY, SERGEANT DREW.
THE END

CONTINUED FROM PAGE 15

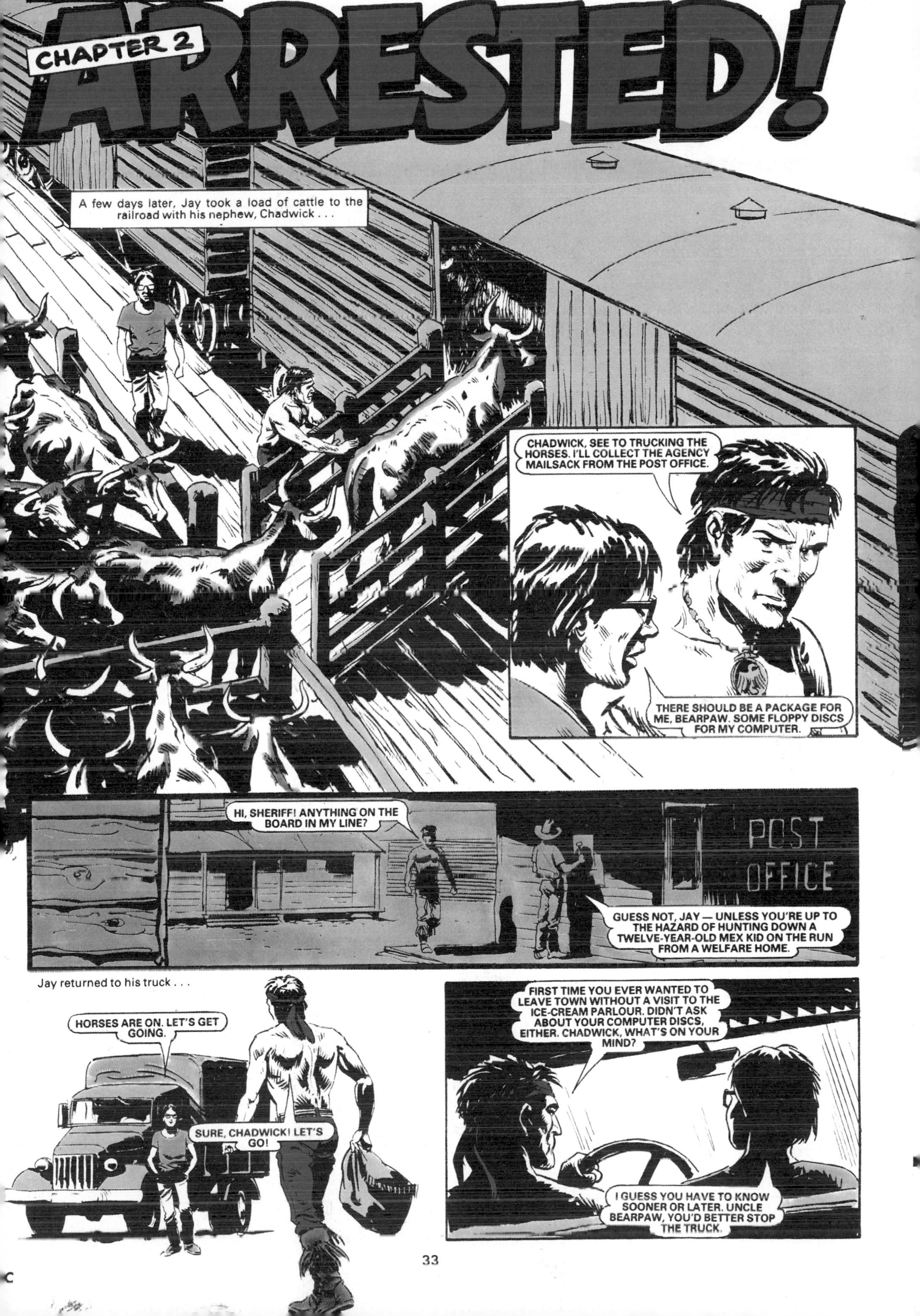

CHAPTER 2 ARRESTED!

A few days later, Jay took a load of cattle to the railroad with his nephew, Chadwick . . .

CHADWICK, SEE TO TRUCKING THE HORSES. I'LL COLLECT THE AGENCY MAILSACK FROM THE POST OFFICE.

THERE SHOULD BE A PACKAGE FOR ME, BEARPAW. SOME FLOPPY DISCS FOR MY COMPUTER.

HI, SHERIFF! ANYTHING ON THE BOARD IN MY LINE?

POST OFFICE

GUESS NOT, JAY — UNLESS YOU'RE UP TO THE HAZARD OF HUNTING DOWN A TWELVE-YEAR-OLD MEX KID ON THE RUN FROM A WELFARE HOME.

Jay returned to his truck . . .

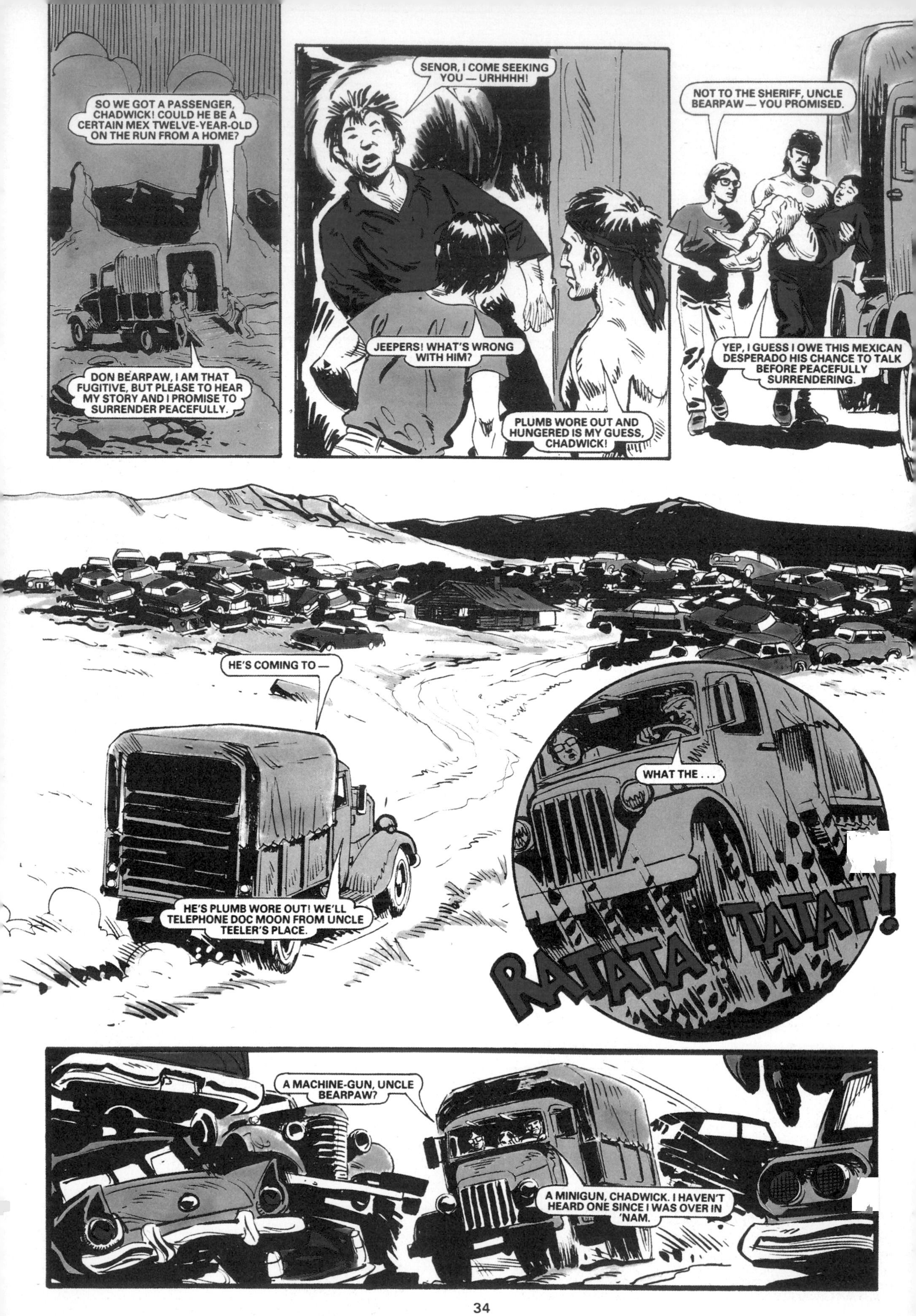

HE'S COMING TO —

HE'S PLUMB WORE OUT! WE'LL TELEPHONE DOC MOON FROM UNCLE TEELER'S PLACE.

WHAT THE . . .

RATATA TATAT!

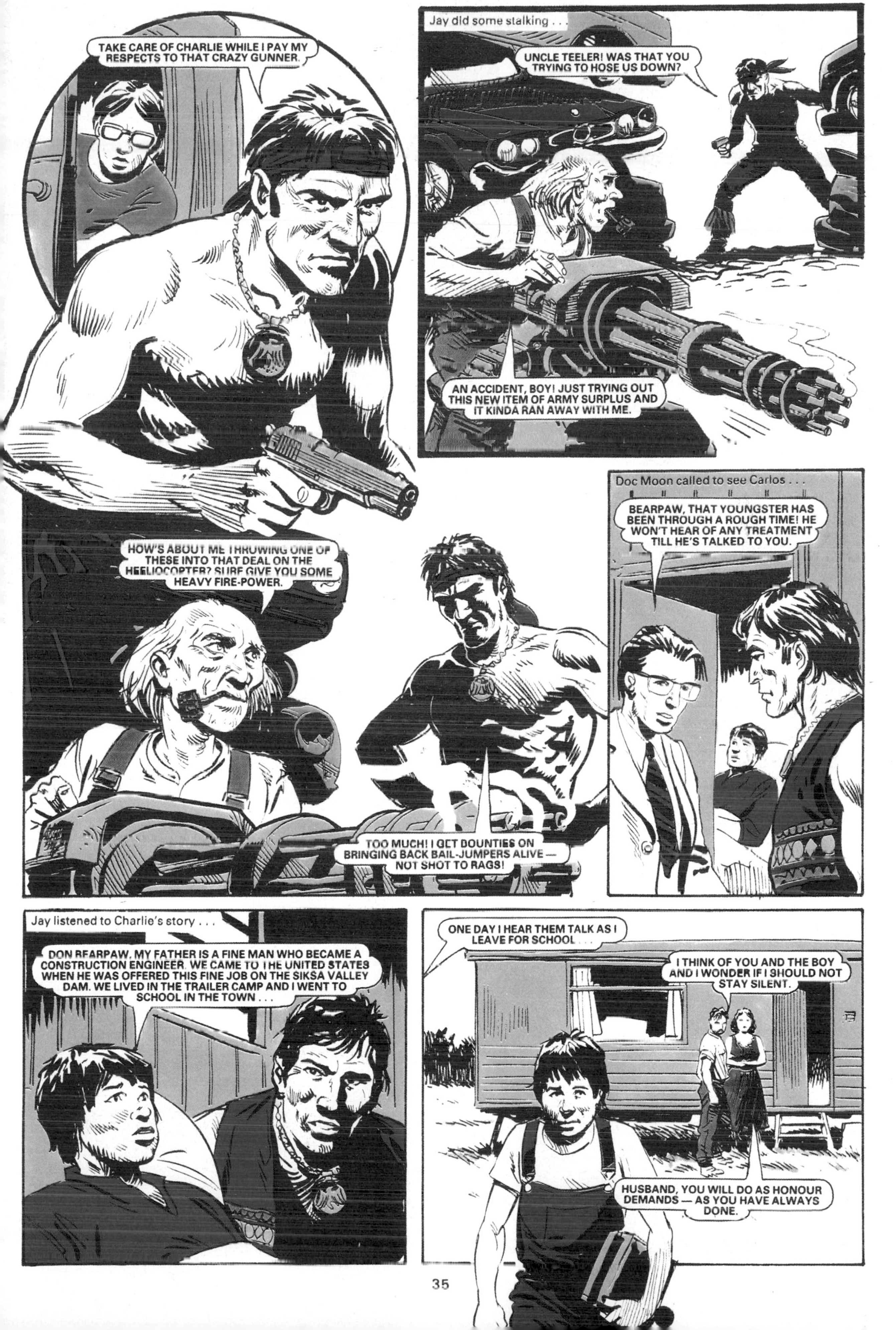

TAKE CARE OF CHARLIE WHILE I PAY MY RESPECTS TO THAT CRAZY GUNNER.

Jay did some stalking . . .

UNCLE TEELER! WAS THAT YOU TRYING TO HOSE US DOWN?

AN ACCIDENT, BOY! JUST TRYING OUT THIS NEW ITEM OF ARMY SURPLUS AND IT KINDA RAN AWAY WITH ME.

HOW'S ABOUT ME THROWING ONE OF THESE INTO THAT DEAL ON THE HEELIOCOPTER? SURE GIVE YOU SOME HEAVY FIRE-POWER.

TOO MUCH! I GET BOUNTIES ON BRINGING BACK BAIL-JUMPERS ALIVE — NOT SHOT TO RAGS!

Doc Moon called to see Carlos . . .

BEARPAW, THAT YOUNGSTER HAS BEEN THROUGH A ROUGH TIME! HE WON'T HEAR OF ANY TREATMENT TILL HE'S TALKED TO YOU.

THE LAST TIME I SEE THEM! I COME BACK FROM SCHOOL AND THEY ARE GONE! I AM HANDED OVER TO THE WELFARE. THEY SAY I AM ABANDONED! BUT NO, I KNOW MY PARENTS WOULD NOT GO OFF AND LEAVE ME. I RUN AWAY AND SEARCH AND THEN ONE DAY I HEAR OF YOU, THE GREAT HUNTER.

TWO DOLLARS, FIFTEEN CENTS — ALL THE MONEY I HAVE. DON BEARPAW — PLEASE FIND MY MOTHER AND MY FATHER . . . AAH . . .

DOC — YOUR PATIENT IS NOW READY FOR TREATMENT!

ARE YOU TAKING THE CASE, UNCLE BEARPAW?

CHADWICK, THAT KID HELD ON TO THIS TWO DOLLARS, FIFTEEN CENTS EVEN WHEN HE WAS STARVING. I DON'T SEE HOW I CAN TURN DOWN SUCH VALUE.

Jay did some telephoning . . .

I AM MISTER PEABODY, THE SOCIAL WORKER ON THE CASE.

MISTER PEABODY, THE CASE IS A LOST SMALL BOY WHO IS SAFE, BUT SICK. NOW WHAT HAVE YOU BEEN DOING TO LOCATE THOSE MISSING PARENTS?

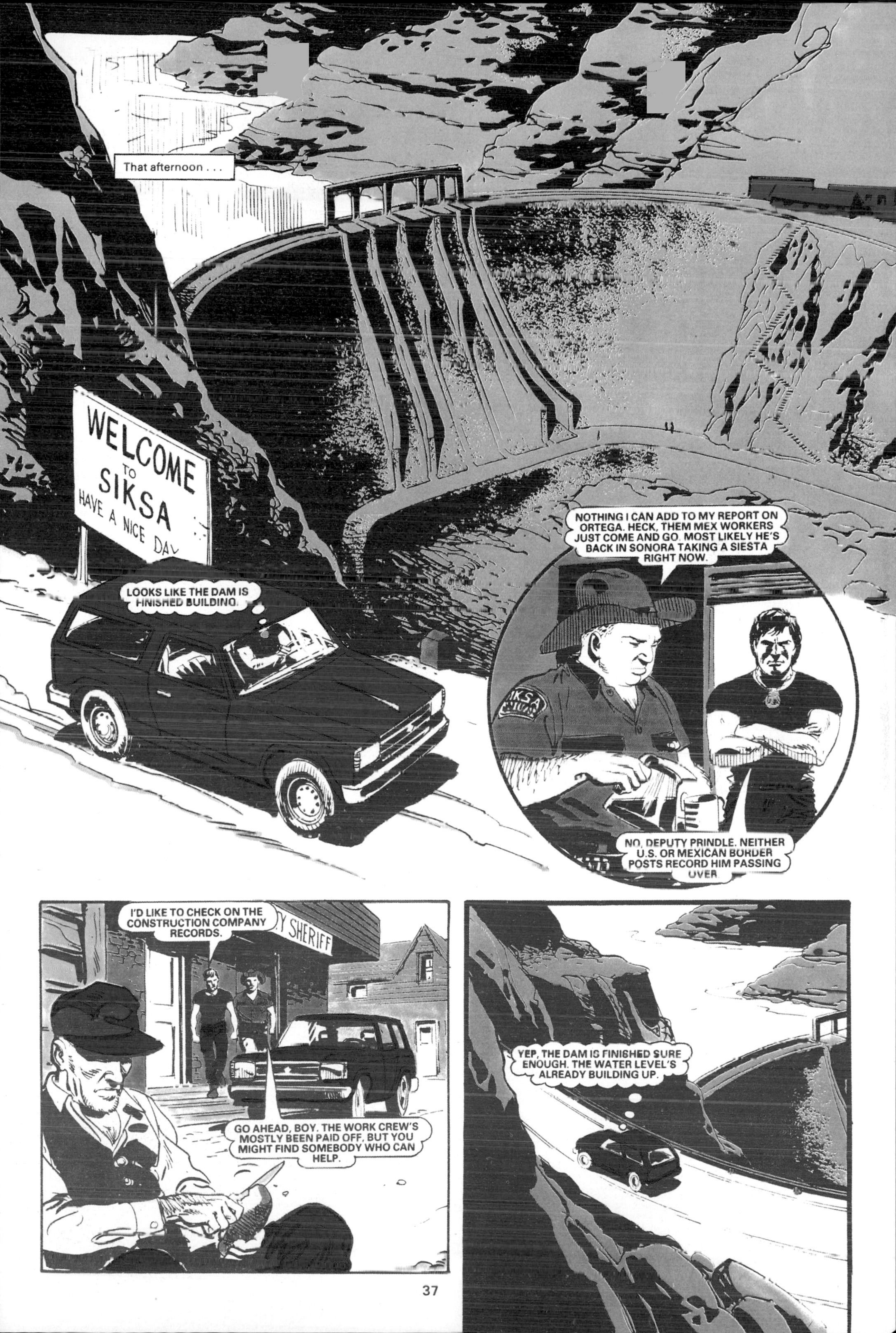

That afternoon . . .

WELCOME TO SIKSA HAVE A NICE DA

LOOKS LIKE THE DAM IS FINISHED BUILDING.

NOTHING I CAN ADD TO MY REPORT ON ORTEGA. HECK, THEM MEX WORKERS JUST COME AND GO. MOST LIKELY HE'S BACK IN SONORA TAKING A SIESTA RIGHT NOW.

NO, DEPUTY PRINDLE. NEITHER U.S. OR MEXICAN BORDER POSTS RECORD HIM PASSING OVER

I'D LIKE TO CHECK ON THE CONSTRUCTION COMPANY RECORDS.
SHERIFF
GO AHEAD, BOY. THE WORK CREW'S MOSTLY BEEN PAID OFF, BUT YOU MIGHT FIND SOMEBODY WHO CAN HELP.

YEP, THE DAM IS FINISHED SURE ENOUGH. THE WATER LEVEL'S ALREADY BUILDING UP.

ORTEGA, EH! ALL I KNOW IS HE WAS PAID OFF AND HE TOOK OFF. THOSE MEXICANS DO IT ALL THE TIME.
SO I'VE BEEN TOLD ALREADY, MISTER DYER.

HOW DO I GET IN TOUCH WITH THE BOSS?
CONSTRUCTION
BY GOING TO EUROPE. MISTER ANDY BUNKER WENT OFF SOON AS THE DAM WAS FINISHED!

Jay visited a bank . . .
MISTER ORTEGA CLEARED HIS ACCOUNT ON THE DAY IN QUESTION. THERE'S NO QUESTION OF THAT NOT BEING HIS SIGNATURE.
NO, SIR, THE WRITING MATCHES. I AM MUCH OBLIGED.

SISKA CREDIT LOAN
MAY AS WELL VISIT THE TRAILER CAMP BEFORE I GO BACK TO FACE THAT KID.

SO THE ORTEGAS DIDN'T CANCEL THEIR VAN IN PERSON! THEY JUST SLIPPED A NOTE UNDER YOUR DOOR!
DIDN'T EVEN ASK FOR THEIR DEPOSIT BACK. NOT THAT THEY'D HAVE GOT IT THE STATE THEY LEFT THAT VAN. THE INSIDE WAS JUMBLED UP AND FURNITURE RIPPED LIKE A TWISTER HAD BLOWN THROUGH THERE!

EVEN LEFT A FEW BELONGINGS IF YOU'RE INTERESTED.
ALL OF A SUDDEN I'M REAL INTERESTED! SOUNDS TO ME LIKE THE VAN WAS SEARCHED.

Jay gathered up the belongings . . .
BOOKS AND A FEW BITS OF CLOTHING. BE WORTH LOOKING THROUGH — THOUGH I GUESS ANY SEARCHER'S ALREADY DONE THAT!

THIS LOOKS LIKE TROUBLE!

OUTA THERE, INJUN. WE WANNA LITTLE TALK WITH YOU.
WHY SURELY, SIR! US REDSKINS ARE GREAT ONES FOR INTELLECTUAL DISCOURSE.
HERE I COME!
URGH!
SO FAR THIS CONVERSATION AIN'T UP TO MUCH.
URGH!
DEPUTY PRINDLE! WHO SAYS THERE'S NEVER A COP AROUND WHEN YOU NEED ONE?
RIGHT, GENTS, NOW WHAT'LL WE TALK ABOUT?
WE'LL START WITH THE SUBJECT OF A SMART ALEC INJUN WITH A RIOT-GUN POINTED AT HIM.
UP AGAINST THE AUTO, BUSTER. SPREAD 'EM AND FREEZE.

CONTINUED ON PAGE 65

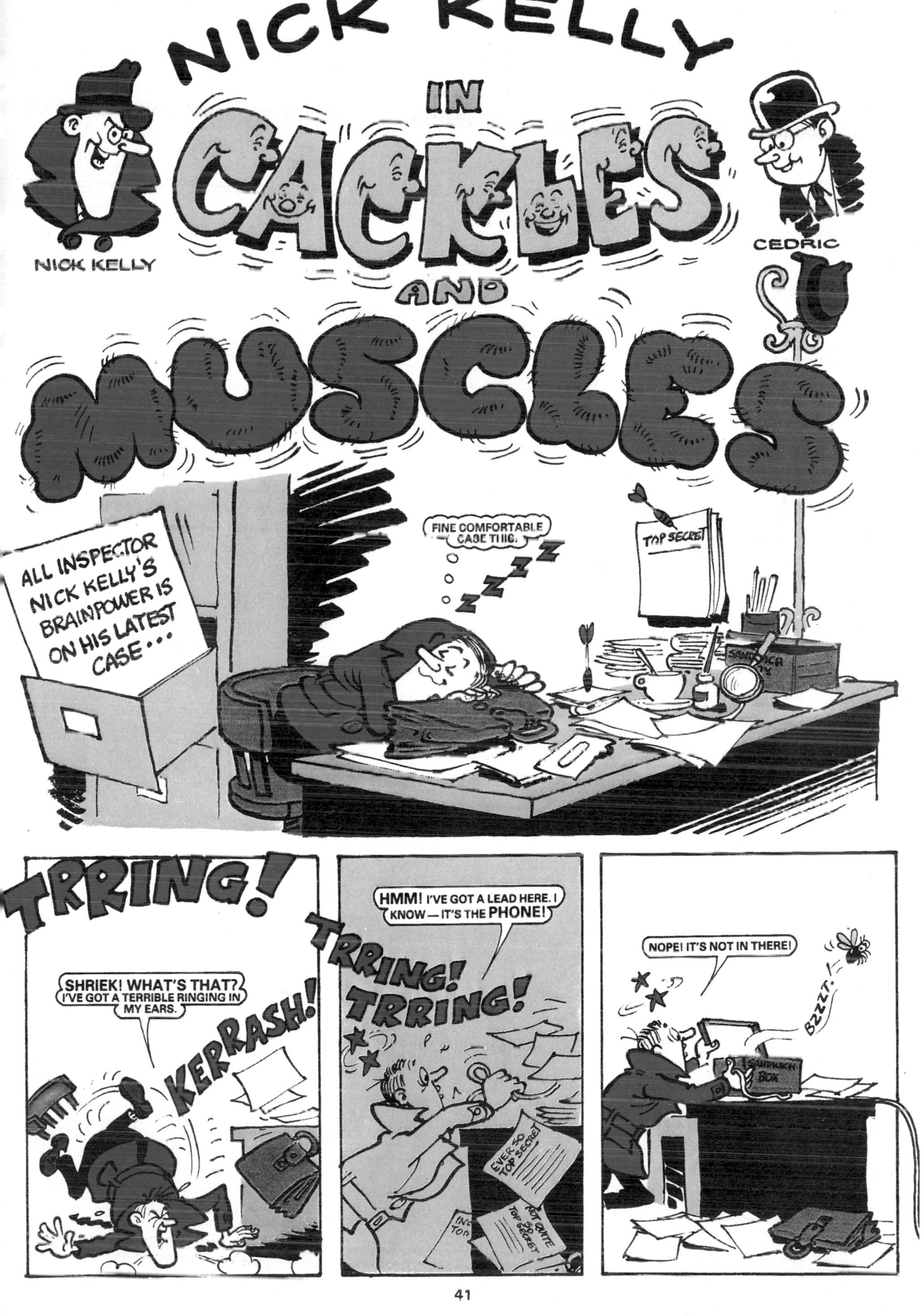

NICK KELLY IN CACKLES AND MUSCLES

NICK KELLY

CEDRIC

ALL INSPECTOR NICK KELLY'S BRAINPOWER IS ON HIS LATEST CASE...

FINE COMFORTABLE CASE THIS.

ZZZZ

TOP SECRET

AND I'VE NOT GOT IT.
TRRING!

TRRING!
OF COURSE!

HERE IT IS. GOOD, THERE'S NO QUEUE.
TELEPHONE

HELLO, HELLO . . .

HELLO! I'VE BEEN RINGING YOUR DOORBELL FOR AGES!
TELEPHONE
AHEM! BELLS ALL SOUND THE SAME TO ME. WHAT CAN I DO FOR YOU, MADAM?

SOB! IT'S MY HUSBAND. WAIL!
IT IS? WHERE?

I'M WORRIED ABOUT HIM. THIS IS HIM LAST WEEK.
HE SEEMS A NICE ENOUGH CHAP.

I'VE ANOTHER PICTURE TO SHOW YOU THOUGH.

THIS IS A PICTURE OF HIM THIS WEEK!
WOW! THERE'S SOMETHING DIFFERENT ABOUT HIM. IT'S THE HAIRSTYLE, ISN'T IT?

I WAS ONLY JOKING, OF COURSE. PLEASE TELL ME ALL ABOUT IT QUICKLY BEFORE MY FEES GO UP.
WELL, HE WAS TIRED BEING A SEVEN STONE WEAKLING, SO HE JOINED A HEALTH AND FITNESS CLUB THAT SUDDENLY OPENED IN TOWN.

SOB! IT TURNED HIM INTO A NASTY, MEAN, EVIL VILLAIN WITH BIG, BIG, QUITE NICE MUSCLES. SNIFF!
THIS COULD BE AN INTERESTING CASE. I'M FED-UP OF THAT LEATHER ONE ALREADY.

I JUST WANT HIM BACK . . . SOB . . . THE WAY HE WAS. SNIFFLE!
THERE, THERE, MADAM. HERE, USE THIS.

OH, NO! NOT ON MY BEST SHIRT.
SCHONORPH!

WILL YOU HELP FIND OUT WHAT'S HAPPENED TO MY HUSBAND, MR KELLY?
CERTAINLY, MADAM. I WON'T EVEN CHARGE YOU FOR A NEW SHIRT. I'LL GET MY ASSISTANT CEDRIC, TO ASSIST ME ON THE CASE.

Soon after —
CEDRIC! THIS IS YOUR BOSS, DETECTIVE NICK KELLY, SPEAKING! REPORT TO BASE IMMEDIATELY!
WOW! A DETECTIVE! RUN! WE WERE BEING FOLLOWED!
SIGH! COMING, MR KELLY.

I'D LIKE YOU TO HELP ME ON THIS CASE, CEDRIC.
VERY WELL, MR KELLY. I'M YOUR MAN!

THANKS, CEDRIC. YOU'VE BEEN A GREAT HELP.
HMPH! THIS ISN'T QUITE THE CASE I HAD IN MIND.

I'VE TOLD YOU EVERYTHING, CEDRIC. NOW TO FIND THIS HEALTH AND FITNESS CLUB.
COULDN'T WE JUST GO JOGGING IN THE PARK?

I THINK THAT OLD LADY COULD BE WANTING TO CROSS THE ROAD, CEDRIC.
BEANO
BRILLIANT, MR KELLY!

EXCUSE ME, NICE OLD LADY . . .
TAP! TAP!

OO-ER! DID I STARTLE YOU?
G-GULP! SHE'S STARTLING ME!

GURR!
THERE'S NOTHING FRAIL ABOUT THIS OLD LADY, CEDRIC.
SHE LOOKS LIKE ARNOLD SCHWARZENEGGER'S GRANNY!

SHE SEEMS TO BE DOING FINE IN THE TRAFFIC BY HERSELF, CEDRIC.
STOMP! STOMP!

IT'S THE END OF THE ROAD FOR YOU, BOYS.
CRASH!
AAARGH! I THINK SHE'S BEEN TO THE CLUB WE'RE LOOKING FOR, CEDRIC.
YEEOW! EVERY DAY FOR WEEKS, I'D SAY.
A731 SFB

After being dropped off —

MIND IF I POP IN HERE, MR KELLY? I'VE A BOOK TO RETURN.
LIBRARY
SIGH! WELL BE QUICK, CEDRIC.

EXCUSE ME, GOOD LIBRARIAN. I'D LIKE TO RETURN THIS BOOK. I FORGOT I HAD IT.
SPLUTTER! THAT BOOK'S BEEN OUT FOR SEVEN YEARS NOW.

SNARL!
OKAY, OKAY. I'LL PAY THE FINE.
HOW TO IMPROVE YOUR MEMORY

ROAR!
SILENCE
SSH! YOU'RE SETTING A BAD EXAMPLE TO THE PUBLIC.

MUNCH!
CHOMP!
OO-ER! WILL IT HELP IF I SAY I'M SORRY?
WHAT DID I SAY?
HMM! EXACTLY! I THINK I SEE A COMMON LINK HERE.
CRUNCH!
CRASH!
GRIND!
SILENCE
THE WORDS 'EXCUSE ME' SEEMED TO TRIGGER OFF BOTH OF THEM AND TURN THEM INTO RAGING HULKS. THAT IS THE LINK.
I THINK HE'S THE MISSING LINK.
SOMEWHERE, FOLK ARE BEING BRAINWASHED AND TURNED INTO HULKS.
YES, AND I'VE MY SUSPICIONS IT'S THAT HEALTH AND FITNESS CLUB WE'RE LOOKING FOR.
THIS IS THE PLACE, MR KELLY.
HOW CAN YOU BE SURE? THERE ARE DOZENS OF THESE CLUBS IN TOWN.

SUSPICIOUS
HEALTH AND FITNESS CLUB
BY JOVE! I DO BELIEVE YOU'RE RIGHT, CEDRIC.
A SUSPICIOUS NAME IF EVER I SAW ONE.

HMM! NO SIGN OF A KNOCKER!

KNOCK!
WE SPOKE TOO SOON.
KNOCK!

WHAT DO YOU WANT?
GROAN! ER, I'M INTERESTED IN FITNESS AND HE'S INTERESTED IN HEALTH.
MOAN! YES, THAT'S US.

GRAB!
AND I'M INTERESTED IN YOU PAIR OF SNOOPERS.
SQUERK!

HMPH! YOU TWO CERTAINLY NEED SOME OF OUR SPECIAL HEALTH AND FITNESS.
COUGH! ME? I FEEL LIKE A MILLION DOLLARS.
PROD!
WHEEZE! YES! GREEN AND CRUMPLED.

CONTINUED ON PAGE 73.

IRON HORSE IVAN

TROOP WITHDRAW! TAKE COVER IN THOSE WOODS!

Russian tanks were taking a savage mauling from the invading Germans near Vorst in the summer of 1942 . . .

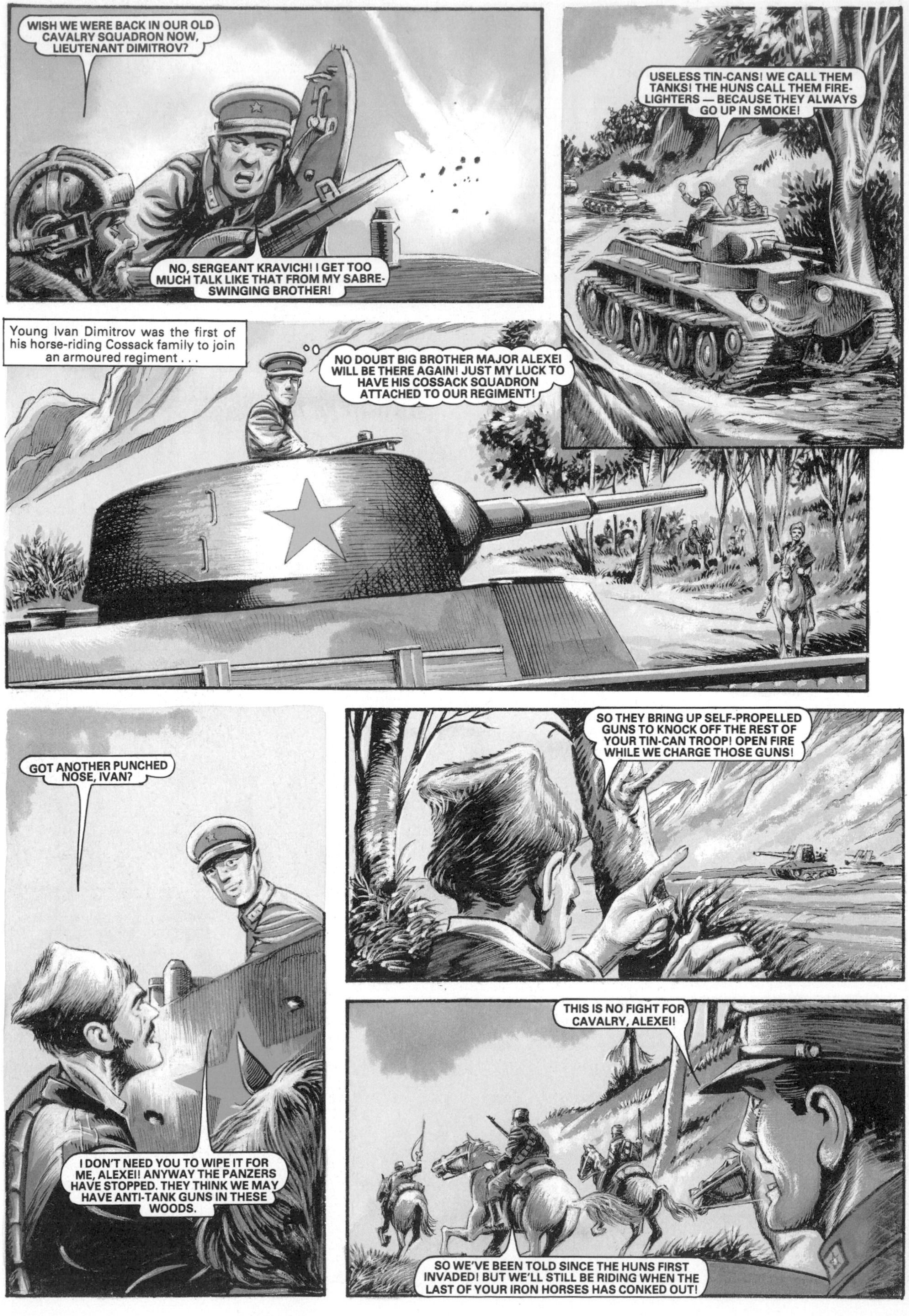

WISH WE WERE BACK IN OUR OLD CAVALRY SQUADRON NOW, LIEUTENANT DIMITROV?

NO, SERGEANT KRAVICH! I GET TOO MUCH TALK LIKE THAT FROM MY SABRE-SWINGING BROTHER!

USELESS TIN-CANS! WE CALL THEM TANKS! THE HUNS CALL THEM FIRE-LIGHTERS — BECAUSE THEY ALWAYS GO UP IN SMOKE!

Young Ivan Dimitrov was the first of his horse-riding Cossack family to join an armoured regiment . . .

NO DOUBT BIG BROTHER MAJOR ALEXEI WILL BE THERE AGAIN! JUST MY LUCK TO HAVE HIS COSSACK SQUADRON ATTACHED TO OUR REGIMENT!

PUT DOWN SMOKE SHELLS TO COVER THOSE HORSE-BRAINED IDIOTS!
HURRAH! CHARGE!

WE'VE GOT BEHIND THEM! DESTROY THE MAD HUN DOGS!

MAJOR ALEXEI SEEMS TO HAVE DONE IT AGAIN!
CRAZY COURAGE AND SHEER LUCK!

That night—
ENEMY INFANTRY HAVE REACHED THE CHEKOVA RIVER. OUR TANK TROOP IS ORDERED TO DRIVE THEM OFF THE BRIDGE THERE.
LEAVE THAT TO MY COSSACKS!

NO, ALEXEI! YOU MAY OUT-RANK ME BUT THESE ORDERS ARE FROM THE GENERAL!
BAH! SINCE WHEN DID COSSACKS BOTHER ABOUT ORDERS FROM THE GENERAL WHEN THERE ARE HUNS TO KILL?

Next morning—
WATCH OUT YOUR IRON HORSE DOESN'T MAKE A MEAL FOR THE HUN TIGERS!
WE HAVE ONLY ENEMY INFANTRY TO TACKLE THIS TIME! THEY WILL NOT BOTHER ME!

ACHTUNG! RUSSKI TANKS!
GO STRAIGHT FOR THE BRIDGE! THERE'S NOTHING TO STOP US!

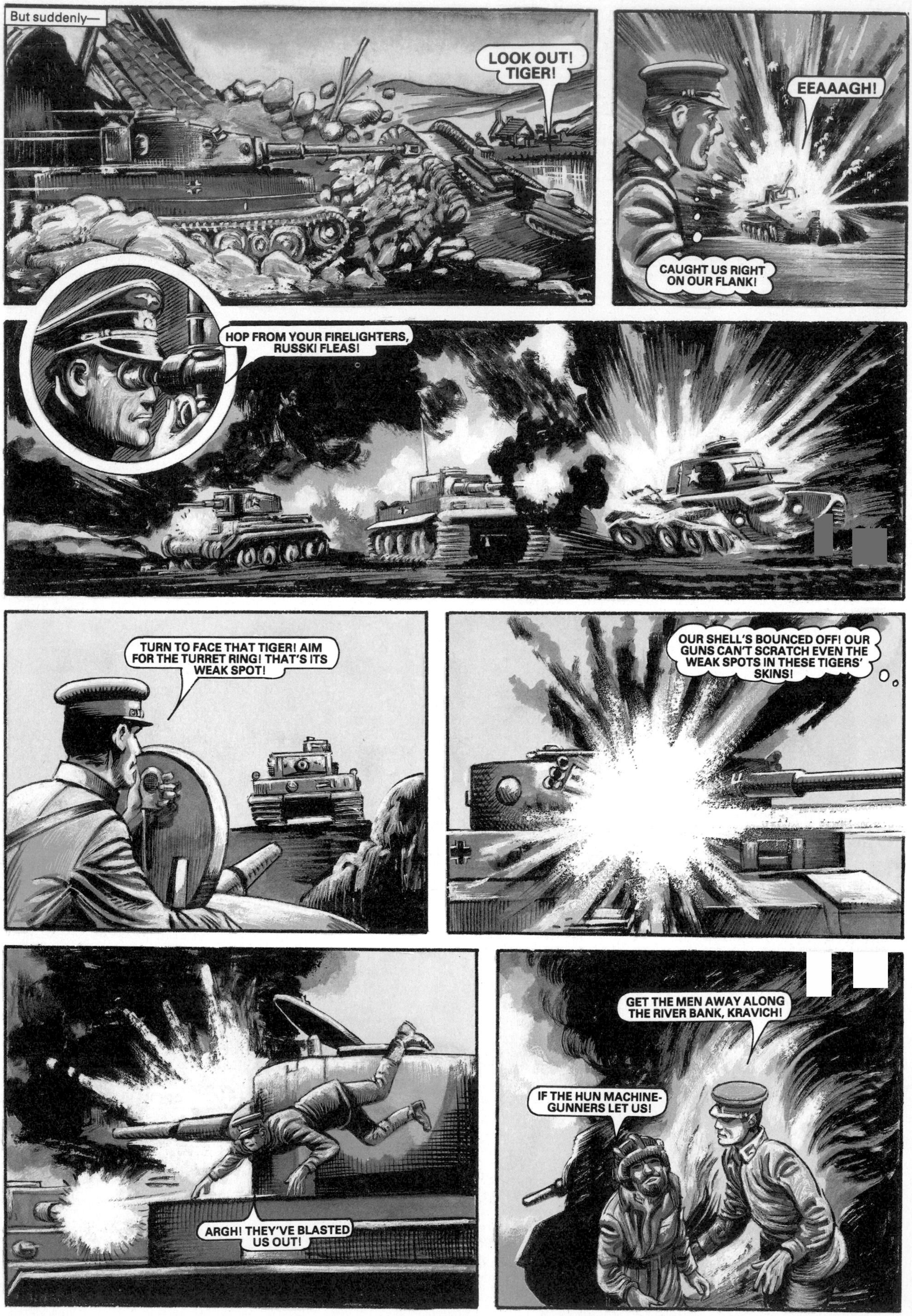

But suddenly—

LOOK OUT! TIGER!

EEAAAGH!

CAUGHT US RIGHT ON OUR FLANK!

HOP FROM YOUR FIRELIGHTERS, RUSSKI FLEAS!

COME, WE MUST GET CLEAR!
RUN, RUSSKI RATS!
Just then—
CHARGE! CUT THE SWINE DOWN!

BROTHER ALEXEI TO THE RESCUE AGAIN!
LOST YOUR IRON HORSE, IVAN? WE CROSSED THE RIVER TO ATTACK FROM THE FAR SIDE. YOUR TANKS COULD NOT SWIM LIKE OUR HORSES, EH?

WE'LL TAKE YOU AND YOUR OTHER WOUNDED TO HOSPITAL. MAYBE AFTER THIS YOU'LL GET YOURSELF A DECENT MOUNT — WITH FOUR LEGS INSTEAD OF TRACKS!

Some weeks later—
FINE PLACE THIS FOR US TO REPORT TO AFTER OUR SICK LEAVE!
NOWHERE IS SAFE IN STALINGRAD, KRAVICH! THERE WILL BE A REASON FOR US BEING HERE!

NOW WHAT'S THIS TIN-CAN COMING?
LOOKS LIKE A NEW TYPE OF TANK. THIS'LL BE WHY THEY WANT US!

THIS IS ONE OF OUR NEW T-THIRTY-FOUR TANKS, BUILT HERE IN STALINGRAD. WE NEED CREWS TO TAKE THE FIRST TROOP INTO ACTION.
MY MEN WILL BE DELIGHTED! WE HAVE A SCORE TO SETTLE WITH THE GERMANS!

OUR GENERAL ZHUKOR AND HIS STAFF ARE TRAPPED NEAR PROSPEKT PARK ON THE NORTHERN OUTSKIRTS OF THE CITY. IT WILL MEAN TACKLING TIGERS TO GET THEM OUT.
JUST GIVE US THE CHANCE!

After only a few hours training in the new tanks . . .
THESE NEW T-THIRTY-FOURS WITH THEIR HIGH-VELOCITY EIGHTY-FIVE MILLIMETRE GUNS MAY PROVE A MATCH FOR THE TIGERS!
YEAH, AND PIGS MAY FLY!

GERMAN TIGERS! SPREAD OUT AND ADVANCE!

PITY TO BREAK THE RUSSKIS' NICE NEW TOYS! OPEN FIRE!

THAT'S CORPORAL RASHENKO'S TANK! ONE SHOT FROM A TIGER AGAIN!

RASHENKO SURVIVED THE TIGER'S CLAWS! FORWARD!

HIMMEL! WE ARE NOT STOPPING THEM!

THE TIGERS ARE BURNING!

KEEP GOING! GENERAL ZHUKOR IS BESIEGED IN THAT BUILDING!

Within minutes—
WELL DONE, LIEUTENANT! NEVER DID I EXPECT TO SEE OUR TANKS BREAK THROUGH A CORDON OF ENEMY PANZERS LIKE THAT!
NEITHER DID WE, GENERAL!

MY BROTHER AND SOME OF HIS COSSACKS!
HEY! WAIT FOR US!
THESE COSSACKS LOST THEIR MOUNTS AND FOUGHT ON FOOT. SUCH CAVALRY HAS NO MORE PLACE IN THIS WAR!

ABOUT TIME YOU GOT YOURSELF A TANK, ALEXEI!
ALL RIGHT, IVAN, DON'T RUB IT IN! ONLY IDIOTS WOULD EXPECT HORSEMEN TO DO WELL IN STREET-FIGHTING! IT IS TIME I GOT MYSELF AN IRON HORSE!
THE END

1959

This Aston Martin DB4 GT was powered by a 3.7 litre David Brown engine fitted with three carburetters. This gave it the capability to do well over the "ton" — 100 m.p.h.

One of the last of the Frazer Nash sportscars, this particular car won the British Empire Trophy in 1951. It was driven by Stirling Moss, who went on to become a top Grand Prix driver.

1953

This Morgan Plus Four had a wooden chassis which was sheathed in steel. In its day, it was a real flyer, being capable of accelerating from 0 to 50 m.p.h. in under ten seconds.

1951

1980

Nicknamed the "mini-Ferrari", the Fiat XI-9 had its engine in the middle of the car just behind the two seats. Although a comparatively small 1.5 litre engine, it could push the car along at well over 100 m.p.h.

★★★★★★★★★★

The star of the 1988 Motor Show was this new Jaguar sportscar. Powered by a 6.2 litre engine, it is to be capable of speeds near 200 m.p.h. and will cost around £250,000.

1988 ★★★★★★★★★★

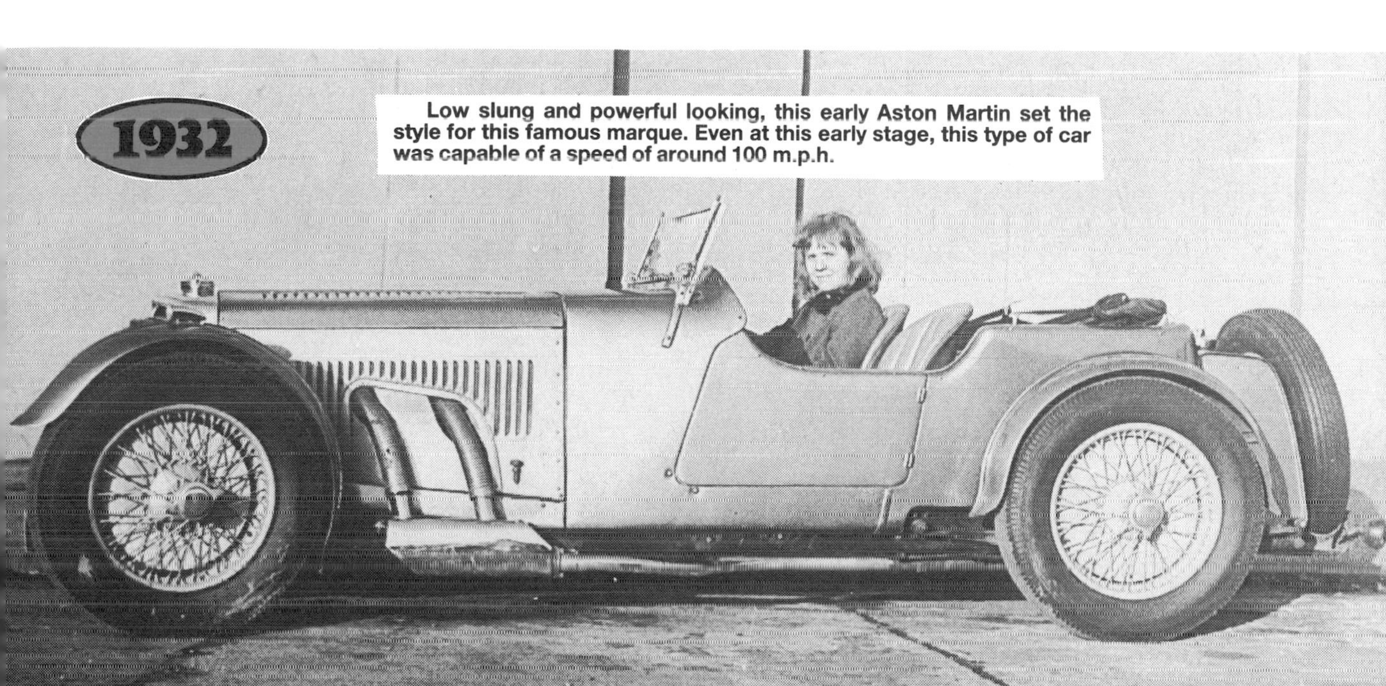

1932

Low slung and powerful looking, this early Aston Martin set the style for this famous marque. Even at this early stage, this type of car was capable of a speed of around 100 m.p.h.

SERGEANT

5
PIKE
The year 2600! An expedition to the mysterious planetoid Kytrone comes to a ghastly end!

A message was flashed to Sergeant Sixty who was patrolling the area with Officer Ben — 688 — Bateman . . .

CONTROL TO SIXTY. KYTRONE EXPEDITION MISSED CHECK CALL. INVESTIGATE!

POLICE

ROGER! ON OUR WAY!

GEE, I SURE HATE GOING NEAR THAT KYTRONE PLACE, SARGE! THINGS KEEP DISAPPEARING NEAR THERE!
YEH, SO THEY SAY, SIX EIGHT EIGHT!

SIXTY

RECKON THEY FALL VICTIM TO THE ROCK STORMS THAT BLOW UP AROUND THERE!

SO THE POLICE COME. TO DESTROY THEM WOULD MEAN MORE OF THEM SNOOPING AROUND BEFORE I'M READY!

HEY, LOOK! THERE'S SOMEBODY THERE! I THOUGHT THIS PLACE WAS UNINHABITED.
ME TOO! IT'S MOSTLY SULPHUROUS ROCK, APART FROM A SMALL JUNGLE AREA.

WELCOME! I AM SEZOR. CIVILISATION LONG AGO LOST ITS ATTRACTION FOR ME. SO I CAME HERE!
PERHAPS YOU CAN HELP US? WE ARE INVESTIGATING THE DISAPPEARANCE OF A SPACE CRAFT IN THIS AREA!

I HAVE SEEN NOTHING — BUT SEARCH IF YOU MUST!
WE'LL CERTAINLY HAVE A QUICK SCOUT AROUND!

I DON'T TRUST THAT GUY, SERGEANT.
I DOUBT IF HE COULD DESTROY A WHOLE SPACESHIP! WHAT'S THAT STICKING UP?

WE'LL HAVE TO HACK THROUGH THAT JUNGLE TO GET A LOOK AT IT!

HHHHHRRRRRH! HRRRRRH!
PUT SOME EFFORT INTO IT, BEN!
B . . . B . . . BUT . . .

GREAT METEORITES! GO FOR YOUR GUN, BEN!

GRAAAAGH!

WAAAAAH! HELP!

THAT MADE IT LET GO!

HE'S COMING FOR ME NOW!

THANKS! NO WONDER ONLY THAT OLD RECLUSE'D WANT TO LIVE HERE!
LET'S GET ON.

HEY, I'VE FOUND SOMETHING. LOOKS LIKE THE TWIN FIN OF A TOY SPACESHIP.
IT'S A REAL ONE WE'RE INTERESTED IN, BEN. BUT KEEP THAT, YOU NEVER KNOW!

AAARGH . . . I FEEL FUNNY!
ME TOO! IT'S THAT VAPOUR FROM THE SWAMP.

JUST AS WELL I FOLLOWED THEM!

WH . . . WHAT HAPPENED?
OOO . . . MY HEAD.
NIPHERTOL FUMES FROM THE SWAMP CAN KILL, SERGEANT. IT WAS LUCKY I CAME ALONG.

THAT WILL CURE YOUR HEADACHE, YOUNG MAN.
YEUUUURGH!

THAT PYRAMID! WHO BUILT IT?
IT WAS BUILT BY ANCIENTS HALF A MILLION YEARS AGO. IT'S INTERESTING FROM AN ARCHAEOLOGICAL POINT OF VIEW, BUT LITTLE ELSE.

THERE'S NO SIGN OF THE SPACE CRAFT HERE — SO GOODBYE! THANKS FOR SAVING OUR LIVES!
IT WAS MY DUTY! GOODBYE!
JUST DON'T RETURN, THAT'S ALL.
P

Two days later the space freighter "Targo" entered the area. Her cargo included a rare honey-like substance called nalopan — a delicacy greatly sought after by the rich of many planets . . .
UNIDENTIFIED CRAFT CLOSING, SIR! COMING UP FAST!
ACTION STATIONS! STAND BY WEAPONS, JUST IN CASE!
TOO LATE! WE'VE BEEN HIT! THEY'VE PENETRATED OUR FORCE FIELD!
WE'VE LOST SPEED.
KILL! KILL! ALL MUST DIE!
TARGO ATTACKED . . . POSITION FIVE TWO TWO . . . AIEEEEE!
QUICKLY! FIND THE NALOPAN.
VERY GOOD, UL, OH GREAT CHIEFTAN!
BEAUTIFUL, GLORIOUS, NALOPAN!

Sergeant Sixty raced to the rescue but . . .
WE'RE TOO LATE, SARGE!
FIENDS! THEY'VE MASSACRED EVERYONE! I WONDER WHO THEY ARE!
THE RADIOMAN DIDN'T HAVE TIME TO SEND A DESCRIPTION OF THE ATTACKERS.
THEY'VE DAUBED THE WALLS WITH NALOPAN.
THAT SYMBOL. I'VE SEEN SOMETHING LIKE IT SOMEWHERE BEFORE.
59
There were further attacks — but never any survivors and never any description of the attackers!
Sixty was called to H.Q. . . .
I DON'T UNDERSTAND, CAPTAIN. THEY STEAL NALOPAN — YET NONE EVER APPEARS ON THE SECRET MARKET!
BECAUSE THEY'VE GOT A GOOD OPERATION, SIXTY. AND YOU'D BETTER GET TO THE BOTTOM OF IT — FAST!
Soon afterwards Sixty came across an abandoned craft . . .
LOOK, SARGE — ANOTHER FREIGHTER.
TOO SMALL FOR A FREIGHTER, BEN!

Sixty went to see Jala, the daughter of Professor Postar who had led the Kytrone expedition . . .

CONTINUED ON PAGE 113

CONTINUED FROM PAGE 40

YOU DID WELL, GUYS. KLEIST — YOU HAD THAT INJUN NAILED YET?
NOT YET, JOE — BUT THERE'S A MAN ON THE JOB RIGHT NOW . . .
. . . HE'LL GET 'IM SOON AS HE'S OUTA JAIL.
OKAY, INJUN, YOU CAN GO NOW! YOU'LL FIND YOUR BUGGY DOWN AT MA BROTHER'S GARAGE, ALL FIXED UP AN' READY TO GO!
AN' FOR A FANCY PRICE, I'LL BET! YOUR KINDNESS IS OVERWHELMIN', DEPUTY!
When Jay got back to the reservation, a welfare worker called Peabody was waiting for him . . .
THIS CUSTODY ORDER APPEARS LEGAL, SIR.
BUT CHARLIE'S TOO AWFUL SICK TO BE MOVED, UNCLE BEARPAW. JUST LOOK AT HIM.
FLOUR! A GOOD WASH SHOULD HELP THIS BOY TO RAPID RECOVERY.
I NEED TO TALK TO HIM, MISTER PEABODY. HE'LL BE BROUGHT OUT IF YOU'LL WAIT BY YOUR AUTOMOBILE.
Jay reported while Charlie washed . . .
THAT'S ALL I KNOW SO FAR! I BROUGHT YOU THESE THINGS FROM THE CARAVAN.
MY CAJA DE SORPRESA! AH, I THINK I LOSE HIM.

HUH — OH, A JACK-IN-THE-BOX!
HAW! HAW!
THOSE OTHERS ARE MY HOMEWORK BOOKS — BUT NOT THIS ONE! IT IS IN MY FATHER'S WRITING.
LET ME SEE IT, CHARLIE.
CHADWICK, MAYBE YOU CAN MAKE SOMETHING OF THE CALCULATIONS IN THIS BOOK.
WHY SURE, UNCLE BEARPAW!
MISTER JAY, I HAVE BEEN HAVING TROUBLE WITH THIS HIRE CAR. I WOULD APPRECIATE YOU GIVING THE BOY AND MYSELF A RIDE TO THE AIRFIELD.
I GUESS THAT'S NO PROBLEM.
SO GLAD YOU GOT BACK IN TIME, MISTER JAY. I HAVE A SPECIAL REASON FOR WANTING TO MEET YOU.
MISTER JAY, KINDLY MAKE A RIGHT INTO THAT DRAW OFF THE ROAD.
MISTER PEABODY, YOU ARE CERTAINLY AN UNUSUAL WELFARE WORKER.
I SHOULD'VE EXPECTED THIS. I GUESS YOU'RE IN THE PAY OF JOE THE PELICAN, PEABODY?
NO HARM IN YOU KNOWING THAT NOW, INJUN — SINCE YOU AIN'T GONNA LIVE T' TELL ANYONE!

HAW! HAW! HAW! HAW!
WHAT THE — ?
AA-AA — TH-THEY SAID YOU WERE A HARD MAN T' HIT . . . BUT THE NEXT ONE'LL GET YOU! THE DAM . . . MOB BUSINESS . . . THEY WON'T LET YOU . . .
HE IS DEAD, SENOR JAY!
I RECKON SO, CHARLIE. THANKS TO YOU AND JUMPING JACK.
MOB BUSINESS — HE SAID! BETTER GO SEE CHADWICK . . .
IT'S A CONSTRUCTION GAME, UNCLE BEARPAW — A DOUBLE PUZZLE! I'VE WORKED OUT ONE SET OF CALCULATIONS ON GRAPHICS!

THE OTHER CALCULATIONS ARE THE SAME EXCEPT FOR AN X-FACTOR — A MINUS UNIT THAT REDUCES THE SAFETY RATIO. ADD IN THIS JOKER AND THIS IS WHAT HAPPENS WHEN THE DAM COMES UNDER PRESSURE!
SO THE REAL DAM COULD BUST OPEN LIKE THAT?
THAT FAKE PEABODY SPOKE OF THE DAM BEING MOB BUSINESS. THAT MEANS MOB MONEY AND CROOKEDNESS BEHIND BUNKER CONSTRUCTION. I'D TALK TO MISTER ANDY BUNKER IF HE WASN'T VACATIONING IN EUROPE.
BUT THE SENOR BUNKER NEVER TRAVELS. HE IS OLD AND HAS A HEART CONDITION THAT KEEPS HIM ALWAYS IN THE BIG HOUSE ON THE HILL.
SO THAT GUY DYER SPOKE WITH FORKED TONGUE. MAYBE IT'S TIME FOR MY RETURN VISIT TO SIKSA.
Jay made a trade . . .
TEELER, DOGGONE IT, I DIDN'T ASK FOR THAT MINIGUN.
BOY, YOU GOT IT OUTA THE KINDESS OF MY OLD HEART. I AIN'T THE SORT OF MEAN MERCHANT WHO ONLY THROWS A RADIO OR SET OF GLASSWARE INTO A DEAL.
A MOB OPERATION, EH! THEY SKIM PROFIT FROM INFERIOR MATERIALS, ALTERED PAY-SHEETS AND A DOZEN OTHER WAYS. ANY PROBLEM AND THE CONSTRUCTION COMPANY TAKES THE FALL!

THERE'S THE SIKSA DAM AND THE WATER'S HIGH. THAT DAM LOOKS SOLID — CHARLIE'S PA COULD BE WRONG IN HIS FIGURING!

TIME I PAID A VISIT TO SENOR BUNKER! THERE'S HIS HOUSE OVER THERE!

A PERSONAL CHOPPER! NOT WHAT YOU'D EXPECT WITH AN OLD GUY TOO SICK TO TRAVEL.

THAT MUST BE HIM — THE SICK OLD ANDY BUNKER.

DEAD! SHOT . . . AND I HAVE COMPANY.

JOE THE PELICAN! I THOUGHT YOU'D BE OUT OF THE COUNTRY BY NOW.
I WAS ON MY WAY WHEN YOU STARTED SNOOPING AND I GOT ASKED TO TIDY UP THIS BIT OF BUSINESS. I SURE WAS TICKLED WHEN THE SECURITY VIDEO PICKED YOU UP IN THE GROUNDS.

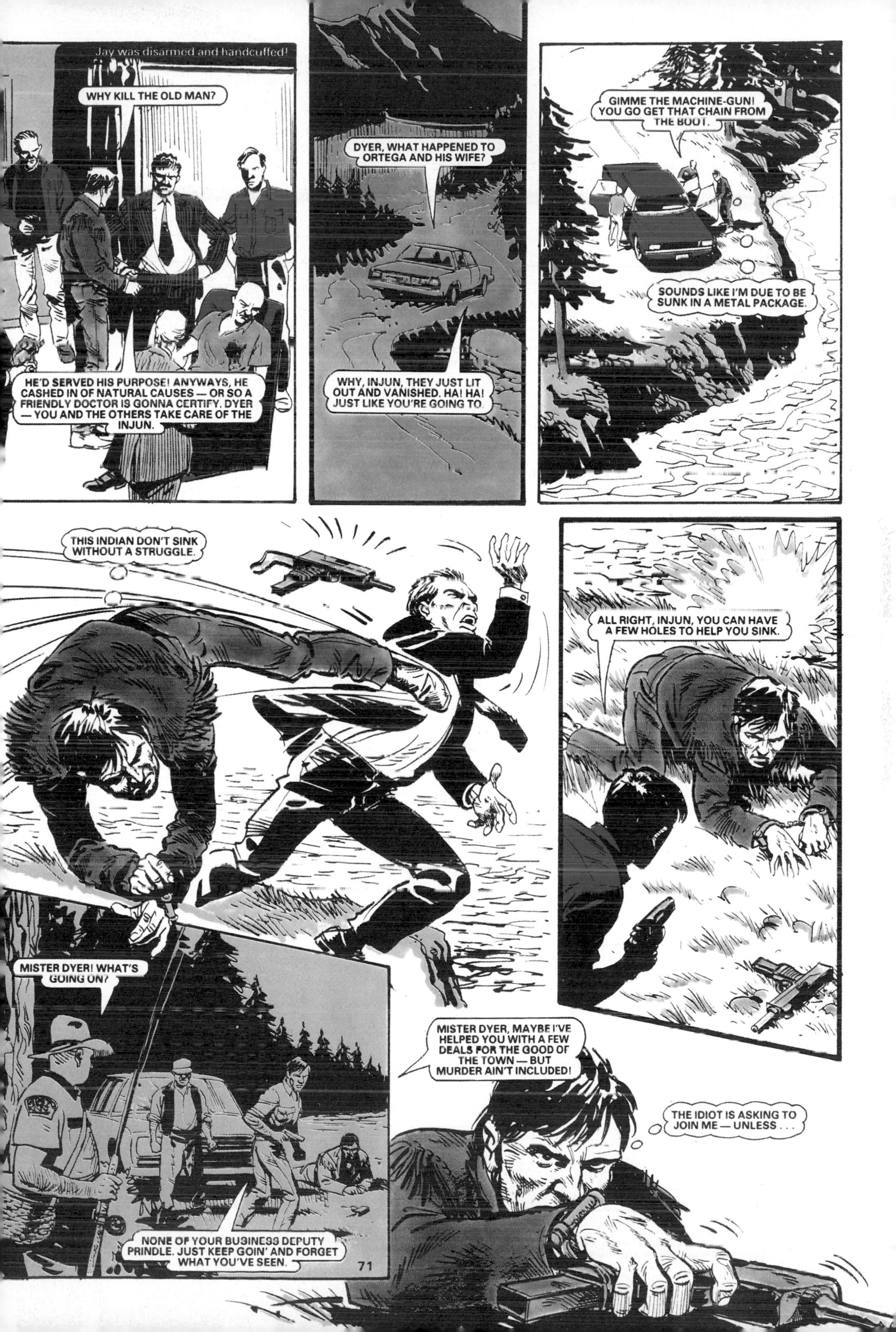

THIS INDIAN DON'T SINK WITHOUT A STRUGGLE.

ALL RIGHT, INJUN, YOU CAN HAVE A FEW HOLES TO HELP YOU SINK.

MISTER DYER! WHAT'S GOING ON?

NONE OF YOUR BUSINESS DEPUTY PRINDLE. JUST KEEP GOIN' AND FORGET WHAT YOU'VE SEEN.

MISTER DYER, MAYBE I'VE HELPED YOU WITH A FEW DEALS FOR THE GOOD OF THE TOWN — BUT MURDER AIN'T INCLUDED!

THE IDIOT IS ASKING TO JOIN ME — UNLESS . . .

Jay headed back to Bunker's house.

BOYS, THAT INJUN HAS MORE LIVES THAN A SACKFUL OF CATS. JUST KEEP HIM AWAY FROM ME!

CONTINUED ON PAGE 97

CHAPTER TWO
CACKLES AND MUSCLES
SNARL!
CONTINUED FROM PAGE 48.
WELL, WOULD YOU LIKE TO JOIN MY LITTLE CLUB? THESE ARE YOUR FELLOW MEMBERS.
GULP! WELL, ACTUALLY I'M ALREADY A MEMBER OF A CHESS CLUB.

MEMBERSHIP'S FREE AND THERE'S A GIFT OF A FREE DRINK OF MY SPECIAL HEALTH TONIC.
OH, WELL, IN THAT CASE, I SUPPOSE.

AFTER YOU, CEDRIC.
RIGHTO, MR KELLY!

BURP! PARDON ME!
CEDRIC! THAT'S NOT LIKE YOU.
YOU WILL FEEL LIKE A NEW MAN.

GROWL!
ULP! THAT'S DEFINITELY NOT LIKE YOU, CEDRIC.
OKAY, MY PRETTIES. SEE TO MR KELLY! YUK! YUK!

IT'S TIME FOR MY FREE SAMPLE NOW.
SNATCH!
HEY!

IT'S NOT FOR ME, YOU UNDERSTAND.
GLUG! GLUG!
HOI! THAT STUFF'S TOO GOOD TO WASTE.

WOOF! MOO! PARP! PARP! COCK-A-DOODLE-DOO!

IT'S A HULK HYACINTH!
IT'S A RAMBO RHODODENDRUM!
BY JINGO! THAT'S WHAT I CALL A SPROUT!
EEK! WHAT HAVE YOU DONE?

SQUEEZE!
OOH! AAH! IT'S CRUSHING ME.
HEH-HEH! THAT FLOWER POWER HAS SAVED MY BACON.

Soon after —
IOUS FITNESS CLUB
THE TIME HAS COME FOR DIRTY DEEDS. I NOW HAVE A FULL MEMBERSHIP!

I'M NOT SCARED, YOU UNDERSTAND. I'M JUST PLANNING MY NEXT MOVE.

STOP! I WANT ALL YOUR LOVELY MONEY!
GET LOST, SHORTY. NOBODY HOLDS US UP! WE'RE ROUGH, TOUGH SECURITY MEN.
SECURICASH

SECURICASH
RELAX, JOE. THIS VAN'S ARMOUR PLATED. HE'S BITTEN OFF MORE THAN HE CAN CHEW.
WOW! WE ARE BEING HELD UP.

CHOMP!
RRRIPP
SCREAM! OKAY, OKAY, THE CASH IS YOURS.
YOU WERE SAYING?

EEK! I'M GOING! I'M GOING!
GURR!
CASH POINT

BANK
THE BIG MUTT WILL GET NOWHERE THERE! HE DOESN'T KNOW THE SECRET NUMBERS!
CASH POINT

CASH POINT
WOW! HE'S CRACKED THE CODE ALL RIGHT.

HELLO! MY FRIENDS AND I ARE INTERESTED IN YOUR LITTLE COTTAGE.
SPLENDID! DO COME IN.
FOR SALE
CONMAN RIPPOVSKI & CO
ESTATE AGENTS

NO, NO, IT LOOKS FINE! WE'LL TAKE IT!
B-BUT!?!

AND WE'LL TAKE THE LAWN AS WELL.
WOW! THAT'S WHAT I CALL A HOUSE REMOVAL.

I MUST GET MY HANDS ON ANOTHER BOTTLE OF THAT TONIC BEFORE DR VILLI VEAKLING DOES ANY MORE DAMAGE.

FITNESS CLUB
THANK GOODNESS THERE WAS ONE LEFT OVER. I'LL GET THIS STUFF ANALYSED AT ONCE AND MAYBE GET SOME MONEY FOR THE EMPTY BOTTLE.

PROF CRACKPOT, I'D LIKE YOU TO EXAMINE THIS.
P. CRACKPOT LABORATORY

IT'S A NASTY ELIXIR THAT TURNS NICE, BORING PEOPLE INTO RAGING HULKS.
VERY INTERESTING. I'LL SEE IF I CAN COME UP WITH AN ANTIDOTE FOR YOU.

Ages later —
AHA! SO THAT'S IT!
YOU MEAN YOU'VE FOUND OUT WHAT THAT STUFF IS?

NO, I'VE SPOTTED THE TERMITES THAT'VE BEEN NIBBLING MY WORKBENCH.
WHAT?

NEVER MIND ABOUT YOUR STUPID TERMITES. THIS IS VERY IMPORTANT!
SLAM!
S-SORRY, MR KELLY.

OO-ER! THESE TERMITES DID NIBBLE YOUR WORKBENCH, DIDN'T THEY?
OH, NO! NOW LOOK WHAT YOU'VE DONE.
CRASH!
TINKLE!

Much later still —
ANYWAY I THINK I KNOW WHAT THIS STUFF IS! I'LL PREPARE THE ANTIDOTE.
YIPPEE! I'LL EVEN BUY YOU A NEW WORKBENCH, PROF.

BUT FIRST, A CELEBRATION DRINK.
EH?

CHEERS!
NO! NOT THAT STUFF, YOU SILLY OLD GOAT!
GUZZLE!

OO-ER! I FEEL A LITTLE FUNNY!
OH, OH! I THINK I KNOW WHAT HAPPENS NEXT.

ROAR!
DRAT! NOW I'M BACK TO SQUARE ONE. THIS IS PROVING A MOST DIFFICULT CASE!

NALDSON
JEWELLER
I MUST SEE WHAT DR VEAKLING AND HIS MOB ARE UP TO NOW!

BANI
OH, NO! THIS IS A TRAGEDY! IT'S A NIGHTMARE!
TO THE BANK, MY HANDSOME HULKS.

BANK
ALL MY SAVINGS ARE IN THIS BANK. NOT TO MENTION MY COLLECTION OF ANTIQUE EGG CUPS.

BANG!
BANG!
NOT TO WORRY, I'VE HAD A BRAINWAVE.

BANK
COSTUME HIRE
NOW FOR A QUICK DISGUISE IN THIS HANDY COSTUME HIRE SHOP.

DUH!?!
HMMM!
COR!
STRONGMAN OF THE YEAR CONTEST—TODAY
NOW JUST YOU LOT IGNORE THAT AND GET ON WITH YOUR LOOTING AND PILLAGING.

I'M THE STRONGEST!
I AM!
IT'S ME!
THUMP! THUMP! THUMP!
ROB THE BANK! ROB THE BANK!
(THROWING A TANTRUM)

YES, LADIES AND GENTLEMEN. JUST LOOK AT THE MUSCULAR HUNKS WHO WILL BE COMPETING FOR THIS YEAR'S TITLE.
HEY! THAT'S US HE'S TALKING ABOUT. IS MY HAIR OKAY?
GRRR! THIS IS MUTINY!
TV

AND THE FIRST EVENT WILL BE THE TUG-O-WAR.
MAKE FOOLS OF YOURSELVES. SEE IF I CARE.
TV

OKAY, TAKE THE STRAIN — HEAVE!
IT'S ME WHO'S FEELING THE STRAIN.

THIS IS WHERE WE LIVEN THE BORING OLD TUG-O-WAR UP A BIT, FOLKS.
WHIZZ!
SNIP!
WHIZZ!

BLATTER!
BLAM!

CRUMPH!
WELL, WE'LL CALL IT A DRAW! THAT EVENT REALLY BROUGHT THE HOUSE DOWN!

PEE-PAW! PEE-PAW!
AT LAST, THE POLICE! THE GAME'S UP, DR VEAKLING.
NOT QUITE!

PAW-PEE! PAW-PEE!
POLICE
PANDA CAR TOSSING'S A GOOD STRONGMAN EVENT, EH, KELLY?
OH, NO! POOR CHAPS HAVE JOINED THE FLYING SQUAD. I KNOW . . .

. . . THE MAIN AND DECIDING EVENT, FOLKS, WILL BE PULLING THE NO.27 BUS THROUGH THE GATES OF SCRUBWOOD WORMS PRISON WITH YOUR TEETH — GO!
OH, BOY! I'VE ALWAYS FANCIED THAT.
27
GNASH! WE'RE WELL AND TRULY NICKED AND THAT'S THE TOOTH!

THE END

CONTINUED FROM PAGE 23

Later—
WOW! A DANGER WARNING . . . AHEAD AND ABOVE RIGHT!

THANK GOODNESS FOR MY GOGGLES! THEY IDENTIFIED A FLASH OF LIGHT AS COMING FROM A TELESCOPIC SIGHT.
X-Bow's goggles could translate light into sound through his helmet and warn him of danger.

GAAAARGH!

HE WAS THE MOB'S TOP HIT MAN, X-BOW.
NO MORE, SERGEANT. I THINK IT'S TIME I HAD A WORD WITH A CERTAIN MR GAMBINO.

That night—
THE GAMBINO RESIDENCE AND HE'S IN HIS STUDY!

I WON'T WAIT TO BE ANNOUNCED!

START TALKING GAMBINO — AND WARN YOUR MONKEYS TO STAY ON THE OTHER SIDE OF THAT DOOR.

WELL . . . KUM, X-BOW . . . X-PECT-DED . . . YO . . . WUD . . . CALL!
WHAT THE . . .?

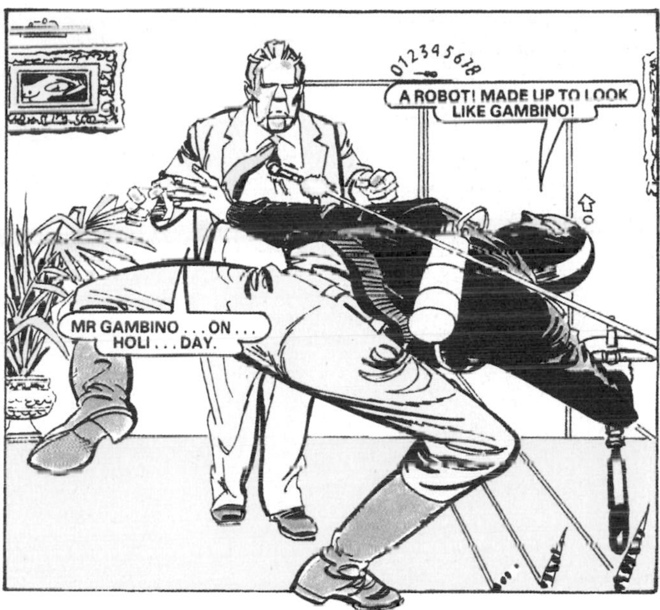
A ROBOT! MADE UP TO LOOK LIKE GAMBINO!
MR GAMBINO . . . ON . . . HOLI . . . DAY.

GOT TO STOP IT BEFORE THAT GUN IN ITS CHEST GETS ME!
I'M TRAPPED! MY ARROW'S JUST BOUNCED OFF!

BET-TER . . . THAN . . . WATCH . . . DOG . . .!
AN EXPLOSIVE DART'S MY ONLY HOPE.

THAT SHOULD DO THE TRICK.

NOW TO TURN THE TABLES!

THE LAW!
DON'T SHOOT! IT'S X-BOW!

X-Bow explained the situation and a few of Gambino's thugs were rounded up.
THE BOSS HAS GONE. HE DON'T TELL US NUTHIN'!
YEH, THAT'S RIGHT!
I RECKON THEY'RE TELLING THE TRUTH.

BACK TO SQUARE ONE! HOW DO I FIND GAMBINO NOW?

Then came a lead from an unexpected quarter . . .
X-BOW, OUR INTELLIGENCE SUGGESTS YOU CHECK THE NEXT F-18 FLIGHT FROM THE CARIBBEAN. IT'S DUE BACK TONIGHT!
THANKS, LUBYAKI.

That night—
THAT'S THE PLANE I'M WAITING FOR.

MY BURNERS'LL BE DROWNED OUT BY THE ROAR OF THE JETS!

IT'S THE PILOT WHO SHOT AT ME — AND THAT SERGEANT JOHNSON! THEY'RE OPENING THE NOSE CONE.

WHAT'S IN THAT PACKAGE?

A GOOD PIECE OF WORK, LOOTENANT. THAT'S THE VERY LAST LOAD. NOW WE CAN ALL RETIRE IN LUXURY!
OF COURSE! NO CUSTOMS ARE ALLOWED ON THERE UNDER ANY CIRCUMSTANCES. IT'S TOP SECRET!
MY BUG-BOLT WILL LET ME FOLLOW IT!

THAT'S A HUNDRED MILES WE'VE COME AND STILL NO SIGN OF STOPPING.

Then—

BEAUTIFUL, GENTLEMEN! THAT DOPE IS WORTH THOUSANDS OF BUCKS ON THE STREETS.
THE MAFIA AND THE U.S. AIRFORCE WORK WELL TOGETHER, MR GAMBINO. NOW ALL WE NEED IS OUR CUT!
A COUPLE OF FAN-BOLTS INTO THE WALL ABOVE THE HAY SHOULD STIR THINGS UP!
WH . . . WHAT THE . . .?
IT'S X-BOW. LET'S GET OUT OF HERE.
HE'S LOCKED THE DOORS FROM THE OUTSIDE!
AAARGH . . . URGH . . . THE DUST'S GOING UP MY NOSE, MY EARS.
GURGH! IT'S CHOKING ME.
YOH COWARDLY SKUNK. X-BOW! COME OUT AN' FIGHT LIKE A MAN! AH SAID AH'D BREAK YOH IN TWO . . . WHEAH ARE YOH?
UUUUNGH!
WHY I'M RIGHT HERE, SERGEANT.
YAAAAAH!

THAT'S KNOCKED THE STUFFING OUT OF HIM!
SHOOT HIM!
I CAN'T SEE HIM!
AAAAANGH!
I'VE RADIOED THE POLICE. I SUGGEST YOU GIVE UP, GAMBINO — UNLESS YOU WANT THE SAME AS HIM!
A . . . ALL RIGHT, DON'T SHOOT!
The police arrived within minutes . . .
WELL DONE, X-BOW! THEIR DRUG SMUGGLING OPERATION WAS WORTH MILLIONS OF DOLLARS.
YEH, WHEN THEY HEARD THE F-18 HAD CRASHED THEY MOVED FAST BEFORE THE SALVAGE SQUAD COULD FIND THE DRUGS! THEN TO THROW EVERYONE OFF THE SCENT, THEY MADE IT LOOK LIKE THE RUSKIES WANTED THE RADAR.
I RECKON LUBYAKI'LL BE HAPPY. HE CAN RETURN TO ORDINARY SPYING AND FILCHING TRADE SECRETS WITH AN EASY CONSCIENCE.
THE END

EVEN with his maw's help, Ossie Pringle was still the worst outlaw in the West!
CIRCUS
THE HUMAN CANNON-BALL
Sheesh! The things that some people do for a livin'!

OSSIE the OUTLAW
HEY! I think I just got me a way to get into the gold store at the fort!
And so—
Ain't yer goin' to tell me what yer up to, Maw?
All in good time, Ossie! All in good time!

That's a great idea, Maw! But who are we gonna find stoopid enough to try it?
PLAN TO NAB GOLD FROM FORT SOCKS
TWIT
FORT SOCKS
BANG
Er—well! I think I know somebody!

It's the best idea yet, boy! It can't fail! We'll be rich! An' YOU'LL be famous!
An' I'll be spread all over Texas!

You'll thank me for this one day, boy!

Thar he goes! That's mah boy!

SLUDGE GULCH

Ossie! That was quick! Did ger get th' gold?
I didn't even get in the fort!

But Ossie! It was a good idea! I jus' didn't allow f' the wind, that's all!
The only gold you are gonna see, Maw, is from yer fillings when I wrap this h-yar club around yer gums!

THE "NEW" MANAGER
YESSSS! DANNY KEEN! THREE-NIL! GOOD OLD CITY!
Norrington City were going for an historic double — the First Division title and the European Cup. With minutes to go in their match with Emmerton—
HOW ABOUT THAT, THEN? MAGIC, EH! WE'RE GONNA BE CHAMPIONS!
BOSS!
HE — HE JUST STAGGERED . . . AND WENT DOWN! SUDDENLY!
GET A STRETCHER! AND A DOCTOR! HURRY!

City won 3-0! After the game . . .
HOW'S THE BOSS, DINGER? WHAT HAPPENED?
THEY'VE TAKEN HIM OFF TO HOSPITAL. NO NEED TO PANIC! THEY'RE KEEPING HIM FOR A FEW DAYS . . . BUT HE'LL BE OKAY!

That evening, Gary Fraser, City's central defender, watched the television news with his wife . . .
KEN ROBBINS, MANAGER OF NORRINGTON CITY, WHO COLLAPSED TODAY AS HE WATCHED HIS TEAM WIN, IS A VICTIM OF A VIRUS WHICH HAS CLAIMED SEVERAL VICTIMS . . . DOCTORS EXPECT ROBBINS TO MAKE A COMPLETE RECOVERY BUT WILL HAVE TO REST FOR AT LEAST THREE WEEKS!
DIDN'T HALF GIVE ME A TURN WHEN I SAW HIM LYING THERE!
GLAD HE'LL BE OKAY!

On the Monday morning a City defender Sam Torrie was shaving . . .
DURING KEN ROBBINS' ABSENCE THROUGH ILLNESS, GARY FRASER HAS BEEN APPOINTED PLAYER-MANAGER!
FRASER! THEY MUST BE STARK RAVING BARMY! FRASER COULDN'T MANAGE A FLAMING WHELK-STALL!

When Gary arrived for training . . .
HERE HE COMES! THE GUY IN CHARGE!
HOW'D THEY COME TO CHOOSE YOU, FRASER? STICK A PIN IN LAST WEEK'S PROGRAMME?

TAKE NO NOTICE, GARY! YOU'VE GOT TO EXPECT THAT SORT OF THING! IT'S ONLY A JOKE!
IS IT? DOESN'T SOUND ALL THAT FUNNY TO ME! LET'S GET 'EM MOVING WITH SOME BALL PRACTICE, EH?

WHAT ABOUT ME THEN? I'VE BEEN OUT TWO WEEKS WITH INJURY — BUT I'M FIT NOW! DO I GO BACK IN THE TEAM?
YOU'LL GET BACK, SAM, BUT MEL IRONS HAS FILLED IN WELL IN THE BACK FOUR! HE'S BEEN PLAYING BLINDERS!

I DON'T CARE ABOUT IRONS. I CARE ABOUT ME! MAKE UP YOUR MIND WHO'S IN! YOU'RE SUPPOSED TO BE MANAGER . . .
I HAVE MADE UP MY MIND, SAM. MEL KEEPS HIS PLACE. YOUR CHANCE WILL COME AGAIN!

The next game against Southpool was a tough one . . .
. . . but Mel Irons proved his worth!
VENUE
GOOD HEADER! THE KID'S PLAYING WELL!
It was Gary who found the pressure greatest!
COME OUT, CLEM! I'VE LOST HIM!
IT'S THERE! OWN GOAL! GARY FRASER TOOK A FOOT TO THAT!
WHY DIDN'T HE LEAVE IT? CLEM BRENTON HAD IT COVERED!
At half-time . . .
IT'S MID FIELD WHERE WE'RE LOSING IT! YOU'VE GOT TO WIN THE BALL MORE OFTEN. TAKE THE HEAT OFF THE BACK FOUR! OKAY?
WHAT ABOUT MAKING A SUBSTITUTION? PUTTING ME ON — AND TAKING YOURSELF OFF! THAT'D IMPROVE THINGS!
I HEARD YOU, SAM. LEAVE IT OUT, WILL YOU? I DON'T NEED THAT SORT OF REMARK!

STOP MAKING LIFE DIFFICULT FOR GARY. HE DIDN'T WANT TO SCORE THAT OWN GOAL. HE'S FEELING IT!
HE SHOULD HAVE PUT ME IN THE TEAM! HE KNOWS IT, TOO, DINGER!
City tightened up and . . .
ONE ALL! GREAT GOAL, JOE!
Near the end . . .
IT'S THERE! THE WINNER! DANNY KEEN GOES IN WHERE IT HURTS!
The win wasn't without its cost!
BUTCH WON'T BE READY NEXT WEEK. IT'S HIS HAM-STRING! ALSO, SANDY CURTISS IS OUT WITH A BRUISED INSTEP. AND I DOUBT IF JOE JOHNSON WILL BE FIT! HE'S GOT A NASTY CUT ON HIS CHEEKBONE!
WELL, THAT MAKES ROOM FOR SAM TORRIE, AT LEAST!
Gary visited Ken Robbins . . .
GOOD WIN AGAINST 'POOL, GARY! ANY TROUBLES AT THE CLUB?
EVERYTHING'S RUNNING SMOOTHLY, BOSS. NO NEED FOR YOU TO WORRY.
CITY WIN
NUTS!
I SEE YOU LEFT SAM TORRIE OUT! I'LL BET HE DIDN'T LIKE THAT. DID HE COMPLAIN?
SAM'S A GOOD CLUB-MAN, BOSS. HE'LL BE IN NEXT WEEK, ANYWAY! WE NEED HIM WITH SANDY CURTISS INJURED.

When Gary put the next team list up . . .
SEAN BRADY IN FOR JOE JOHNSON! AND WATSON FOR BUTCH HARRIS! WHO ARE THEY? FRASER'S SELECTED A TEAM OF UNKNOWNS!
NOT ALL UNKNOWN, SAM! YOU'RE BACK IN!
SEAN BRADY'S GOOD! HE KNOWS WHERE THE NET IS! BEEN DOING THE JOB WITH THE RESERVES!

The next match against Chelbridge . . .
THAT KID'S MUSTARD!

City won and the pressure increased on Gary . . .
ONE MORE LEAGUE MATCH, GARY — THEN THE EUROPEAN CUP! CAN CITY DO THE DOUBLE? WHAT TEAM WILL YOU CHOOSE?
DEPENDS ON INJURIES AND WHO'S AVAILABLE. MUST GO . . . OR THE BATH WATER WILL BE COLD.

Before the last league match . . .
WILL CITY CLINCH THE CHAMPIONSHIP TODAY, GARY?
DID YOU CHOOSE THE TEAM FOR TODAY'S GAME? OR WAS IT KEN ROBBINS?
WE CAN WIN TODAY! I DID CHOOSE THE TEAM. AND THE TEAM'S PLAYING WELL WITH ME IN CHARGE. OKAY?
IS THE TEAM HAPPY WITH YOU AS PLAYER-MANAGER?

IF WE DON'T DO THE DOUBLE, IT'S MY HEAD THAT'LL BE ON THE BLOCK! THE TEAM . . . THE FANS . . . THEY'LL ALL SAY IT'S MY FAULT!

City took an early lead in the last game but with seconds to go . . .
IT'S A DRAW! TOWN HAVE SCORED!

WE'VE HAD IT! LOST THE CHAMPIONSHIP BY ONE ROTTEN POINT!
IT WAS A FREAK RESULT! WE OUT-PLAYED 'EM! YOUNG SEAN BRADY DIDN'T LET US DOWN. THAT WAS A GREAT GOAL OF HIS!
SHUT UP! LISTEN! THE RESULTS ARE COMING THROUGH. IF UNITED LOST — WE COULD STILL BE CHAMPIONS!

NORRINGTON CITY COULD ONLY DRAW WITH FORDWOOD TOWN — BUT SECOND PLACE UNITED LOST ONE-NIL . . .
THEY LOST! WE'VE DONE IT!
WE ARE THE CHAMPIONS!

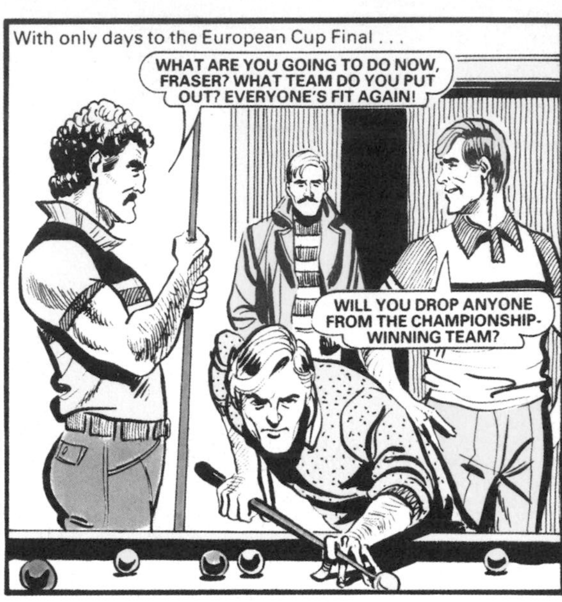
With only days to the European Cup Final . . .
WHAT ARE YOU GOING TO DO NOW, FRASER? WHAT TEAM DO YOU PUT OUT? EVERYONE'S FIT AGAIN!
WILL YOU DROP ANYONE FROM THE CHAMPIONSHIP-WINNING TEAM?

WHY DON'T YOU GO TO THE BOSS — AND LET HIM PICK THE TEAM! YOU DON'T HAVE THE EXPERIENCE, FRASER! LOSE THE EUROPEAN CUP AND YOU'RE IN TROUBLE!
NOT A BAD IDEA. I'LL THINK ABOUT IT.

Two days later, the team list appeared . . .
FUNNY SORT OF TEAM! I MEAN, MEL IRONS IS IN. SANDY CURTISS DOESN'T GET HIS PLACE BACK. AND SEAN BRADY, WHO'S SCORED IN BOTH GAMES HE'S PLAYED IN, HAS BEEN DROPPED!
YOU AND ME ARE IN . . . AND JOHNSON! THE BOSS PICKED THAT TEAM! FRASER DID THE WISE THING AND WENT TO HIM!
SENDON TRANSCOLN

In the dressing room before the European Cup Final in Hamburg against Sparta . . .
HOPE THE BOSS IS WATCHING ON THE BOX! HE'LL BE PLEASED TO SEE HIS TEAM WIN!
SURE! WELL, LET'S GET OUT THERE AND DO THE BUSINESS! GOOD LUCK, EVERYONE!

The first half was tough but City's back four stood firm . . .
GOOD TACKLE, MEL! TAKE IT AWAY, SON! UP THE WING WHERE THERE'S ROOM!
. . . Gary Fraser was like a rock!
OHHHH! OFF THE LINE!
GOOD STOP, GARY!
There was no score at half-time . . .
WE'VE HELD 'EM FOR FORTY-FIVE MINUTES, NOW WE PUT THE PRESSURE ON. THEY'RE PLAYING THE OFF SIDE GAME BUT IF WE RUN AT 'EM WE'LL BREAK 'EM DOWN SOONER OR LATER!
MAKES SENSE!
It paid off . . .
OFF-SIDE, REF!
PLAY ON!
IT'S THERE! ONE-NIL TO CITY!
COME ON, CITY! LET'S HAVE ANOTHER!
ANGLE'S TOO TIGHT! JOE SHOULD BE AROUND SOMEWHERE!

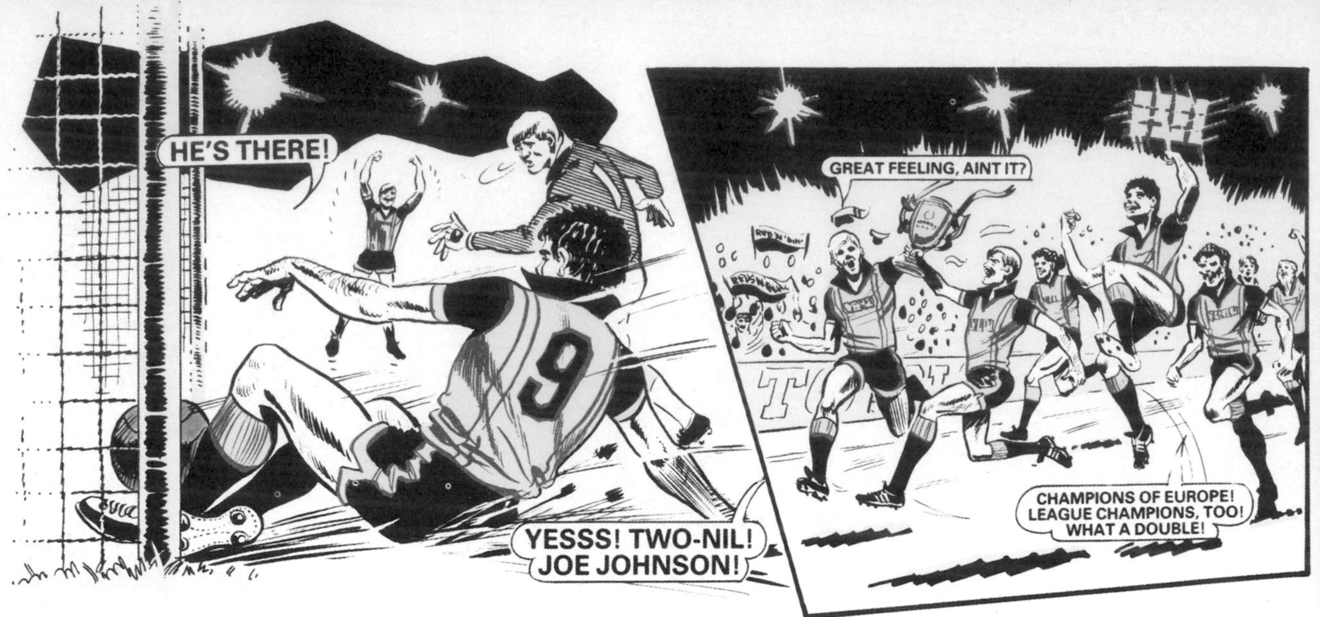
HE'S THERE!
YESSS! TWO-NIL! JOE JOHNSON!
GREAT FEELING, AINT IT?
CHAMPIONS OF EUROPE! LEAGUE CHAMPIONS, TOO! WHAT A DOUBLE!

Ken Robbins, now on the way to recovery, was interviewed . . .
WELL, KEN — YOU WON THE EUROPEAN CUP WITH A GREAT TEAM — AND GREAT TACTICS! THE CREDIT'S YOURS!
MUST HAVE BEEN A DIFFICULT JOB LEAVING OUT SOME PLAYERS, KEN. BUT YOU GOT THE RIGHT BLEND.

GARY FRASER CAME TO YOU AND ASKED YOUR ADVICE, IS THAT RIGHT?
HE CAME TO ME . . . AND I TOLD HIM WHAT TO DO, YES.

I TOLD HIM HE WAS IN CHARGE. AND I TOLD HIM TO PICK HIS OWN TEAM AND DECIDE THE TACTICS. AND THAT'S WHAT HE DID! I HAD NOTHING TO DO WITH IT!
YOU GOT IT ALL WRONG, DIDN'T YOU, SAM? IT WAS GARY FRASER'S TEAM ALL THE TIME! WHAT DO YOU RECKON TO THAT?
I'LL TELL YOU WHAT I RECKON, SON . . . I RECKON GARY FRASER WILL MAKE A REALLY GREAT MANAGER, ONE DAY! WHICH IS MORE THAN I WILL!
THE END

CONTINUED FROM PAGE 72

HE'S GETTIN' CLOSE! TIME FOR WHAT IN 'NAM WAS KNOWN AS EVASIVE ACTION.
NOW TO LET THE JALOPY RUN ON UNDER FULL-CHOKE — BUT WITHOUT ME!

THERE HE IS! HE'S STOPPED! LET'S GET HIM.

THAT'S BOUGHT ME A LITTLE TIME!

Jay reached his own helicopter fitted with the minigun and headed towards the Bunker estate.

THERE'S A FOUR-WHEEL-DRIVE QUITTING THE GROUNDS BY A BACKWAY.

OH-OH — HERE'S THEIR GUNSHIP . . .

POWER ON. LET'S SEE WHAT HAPPENS WHEN I THUMB THE FIRING BUTTON OF UNCLE TEELER'S SECRET WEAPON!

MISSED BY A MILE! A FINE TIME TO FIND OLD TEELER DIDN'T ZERO IN THE SIGHTS.
THAT GUY CAN SHOOT!
TIME TO TAKE EVASIVE ACTION!
HE LOST ME FOR A MINUTE! NOW FOR SOME OFF-HAND SPRAYING AS HE FOLLOWS ME OVER THE RISE.
JUST POINT AND FIRE! DON'T NEED THE SIGHTS AT THIS RANGE!
VARMINT'S TRYING TO CLEAR THE DAM . . .
. . . HE DIDN'T MAKE IT.

WATER! THE DAM'S CRACKING!

Jay headed down Siksa valley . . .
HERE COMES THE INDIAN. YOU GUYS BETTER LISTEN TO HIM.
GUS, HE'S CRAZY. THAT DAM'S GONNA STAND FOR A HUNDRED YEARS.

I CAN'T CONVINCE 'EM.
IN A MINUTE YOU WON'T HAVE TO — THEY'LL BE DROWNED!

LOOK!

TRUCKS AND AUTOS! MAKE FOR HIGH GROUND! MOVE IT!

THE TOWN'S EMPTIED FAST — OH, A BRACE OF STRAYS. LOOKS LIKE A COUPLE OF KIDS WHO'VE BEEN FISHING!
WOWIE! LOOK AT THAT!
GUYS, HOLD TIGHT FOR THE FASTEST TAKE-OFF EVER MADE BY A CHOPPER!
NOW TO SEE HOW YOUR FOLKS ARE MAKING OUT. WHICH IS THE QUICKEST WAY TO HIGH GROUND?
THE OLD MINE ROAD! THERE'S A LEFT TURN OFF THE HIGHWAY.
THERE THEY ARE! SOME OF 'EM AIN'T GONNA MAKE IT!

ONE CASUALTY — AN' THERE'S NOTHING WE CAN DO FOR HIM!

GUYS, YOU CAN TELL DEPUTY PRINDLE I'LL BE BACK WHEN I'VE FINISHED OFF A LITTLE CHORE.

THERE WERE TWO MEN ON THAT OTH CHOPPER — AND NEITHER WAS JOE T PELICAN!
Jay landed . . .
NO USE TRACKING BY AIR WITH NIGHT COMING ON. ANYWAYS, EVEN A SCARED RAT WON'T RISK THIS ROUGH COUNTRY IN DARKNESS.

THAT'S WHERE I SAW THAT FOUR-WHEEL-DRIVE JALOPY QUIT THE BUNKER GROUNDS. AND HE HEADED EAST!

SCRUB THICKET! MY RUNNING RAT COULD HAVE TAKEN ONE OF A HALF DOZEN CATTLE TRAILS.

THIS LEAFMOULD IS SOFT ENOUGH FOR ME TO TRACK THESE TYRE-PRINTS BY TOUCH WHEN I CAN'T SEE 'EM.

AHUH! I GET THE SCENT OF PETROL — AND THE FEELING OF SOMETHING ELSE.
GREETINGS, DIAMONDBACK BROTHER. MAY WE BOTH HAVE LUCK IN OUR HUNTING.

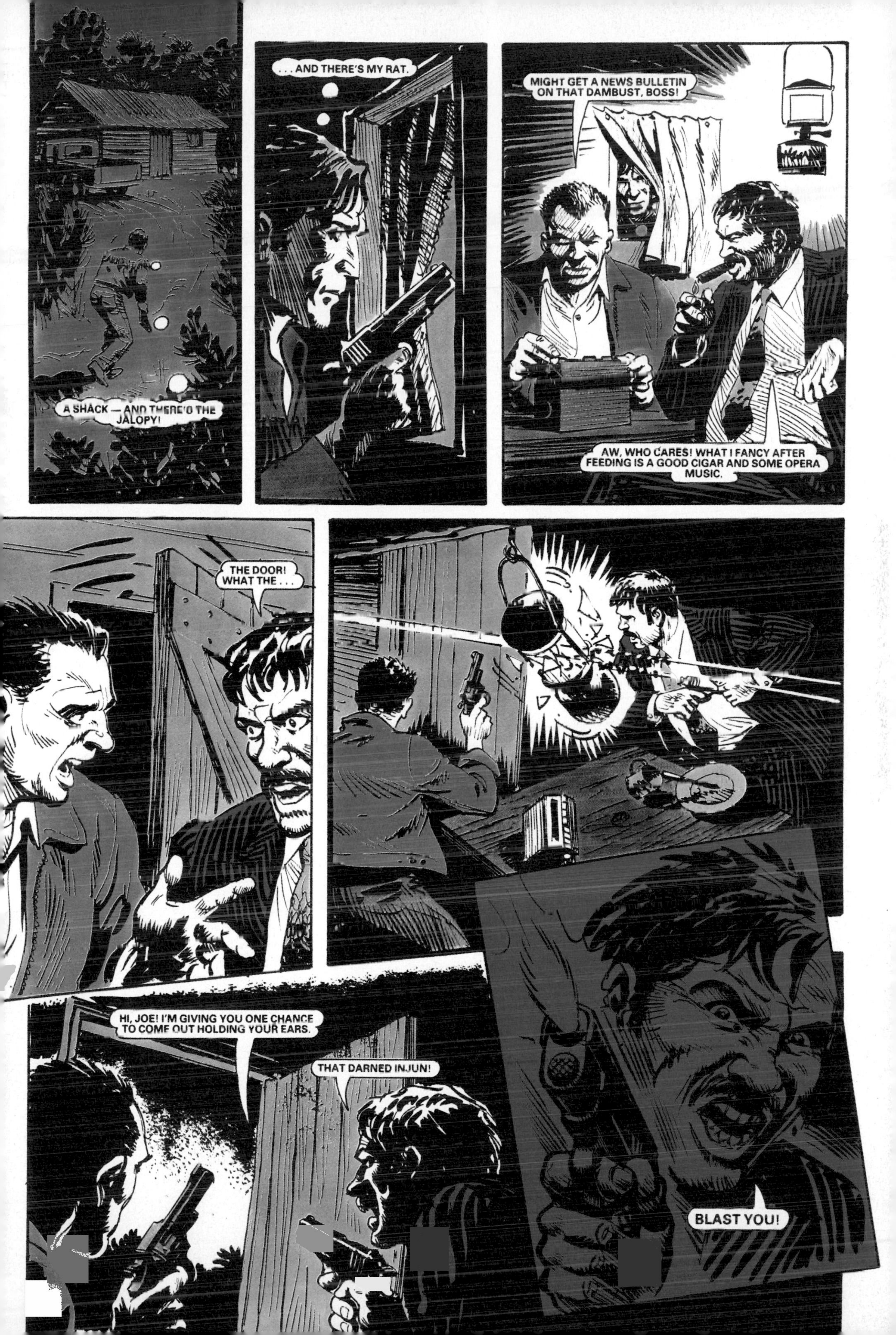

THE DOOR! WHAT THE . . .

HI, JOE! I'M GIVING YOU ONE CHANCE TO COME OUT HOLDING YOUR EARS.

THAT DARNED INJUN!

BLAST YOU!

COME IN AND GET ME!
THANKS FOR THE INVITE, JOE. I'LL SEND IN SOME FRIENDS.

A RATTLER!

GOT IT!
URGH!

INJUN, I GIVE IN! I'M COMING OUT WITH MY HANDS HIGH AND EMPTY.
TOO LATE, JOE! YOU HAD YOUR ONE CHANCE.

SO LONG, JOE!
AW NO — NO!

ARHHHHHHHH!

Next day in Siksa Valley . . .
IT'S A CAR, MISTER JAY. ONE OF THE BOYS SIGHTED IT AFTER THE WATER IN THE DAM WENT DOWN.

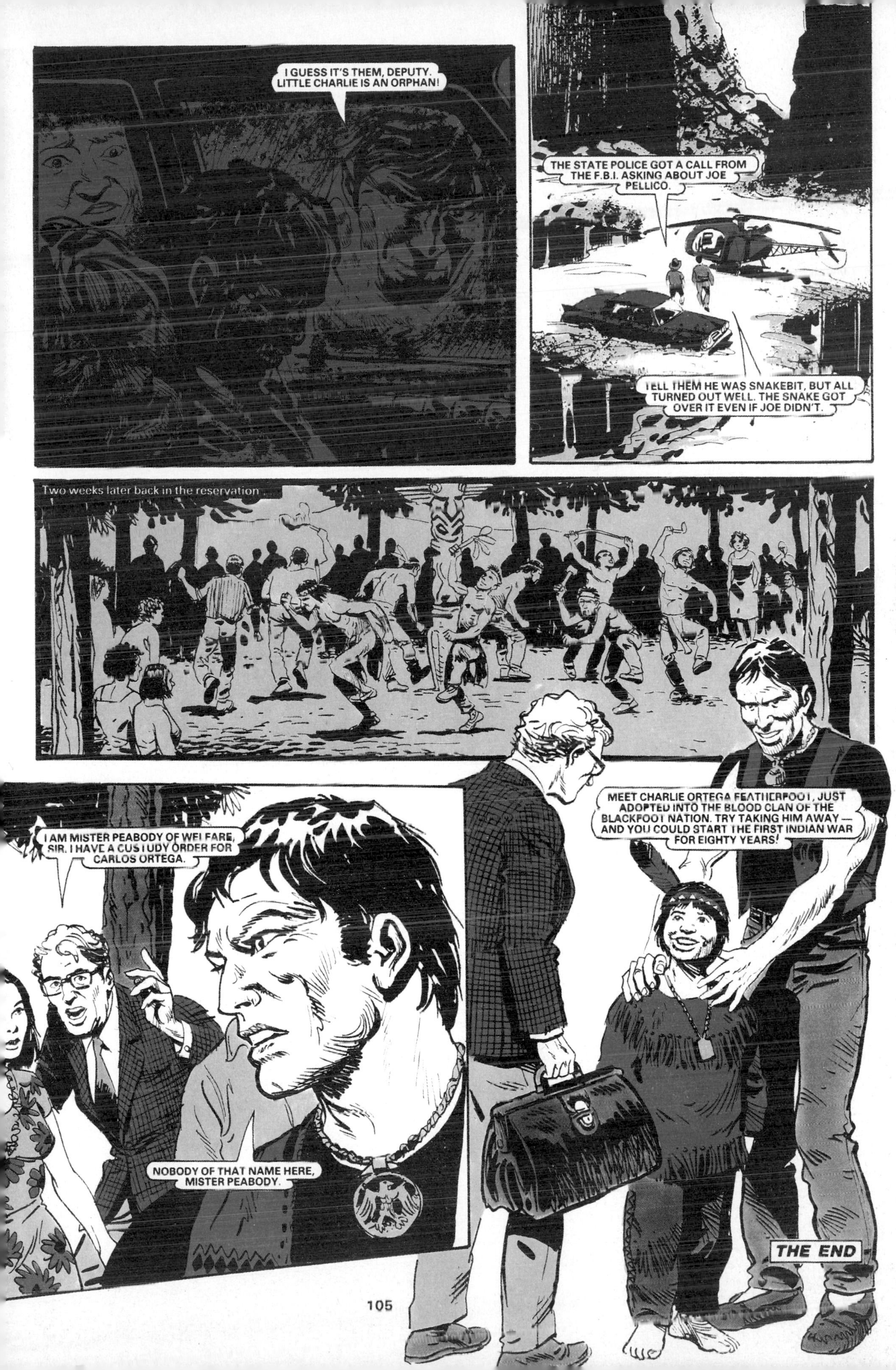

Two weeks later back in the reservation . . .

I AM MISTER PEABODY OF WELFARE, SIR. I HAVE A CUSTODY ORDER FOR CARLOS ORTEGA.

NOBODY OF THAT NAME HERE, MISTER PEABODY.

MEET CHARLIE ORTEGA FEATHERFOOT, JUST ADOPTED INTO THE BLOOD CLAN OF THE BLACKFOOT NATION. TRY TAKING HIM AWAY — AND YOU COULD START THE FIRST INDIAN WAR FOR EIGHTY YEARS!

THE END

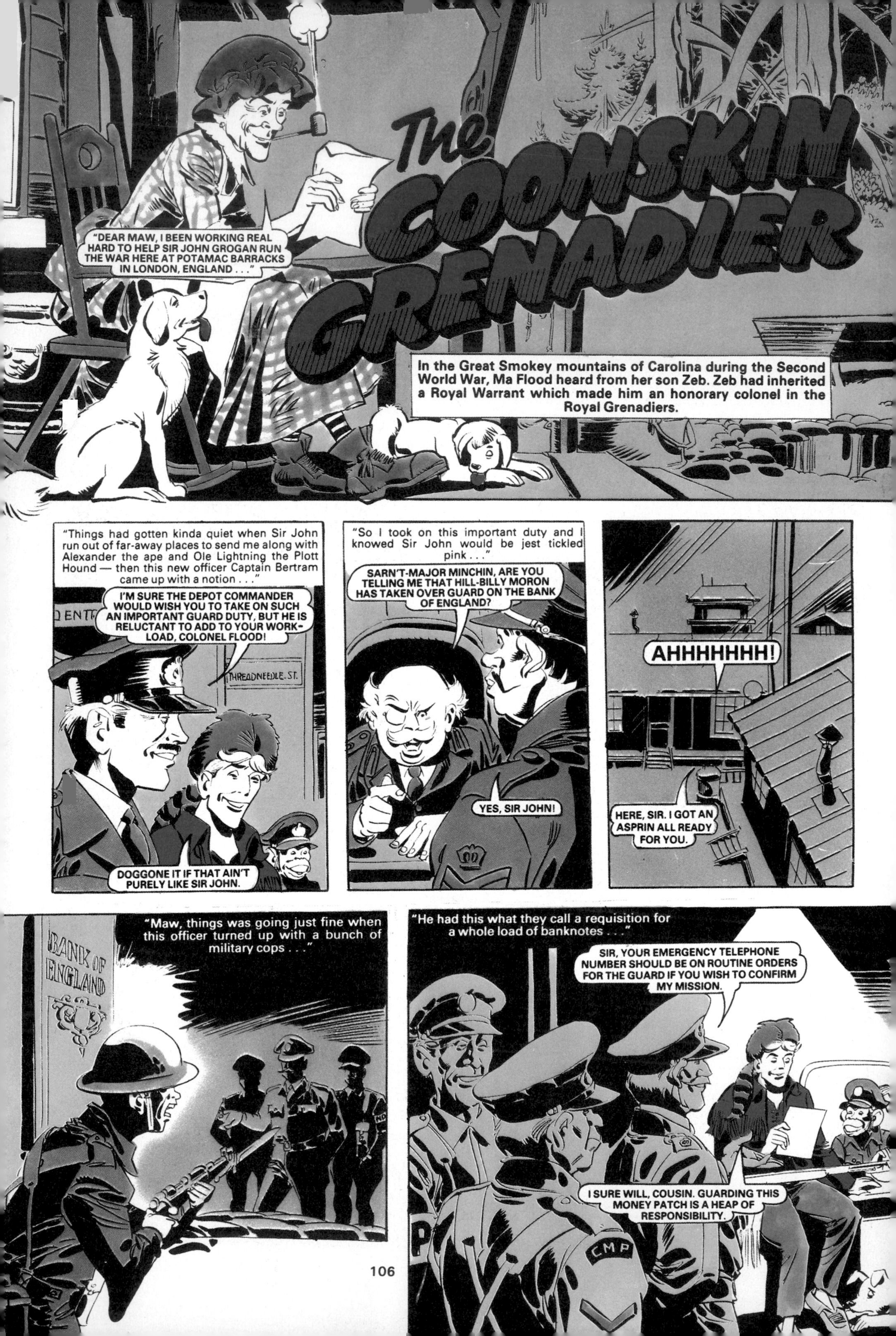

The Coonskin Grenadier

"DEAR MAW, I BEEN WORKING REAL HARD TO HELP SIR JOHN GROGAN RUN THE WAR HERE AT POTAMAC BARRACKS IN LONDON, ENGLAND . . ."

In the Great Smokey mountains of Carolina during the Second World War, Ma Flood heard from her son Zeb. Zeb had inherited a Royal Warrant which made him an honorary colonel in the Royal Grenadiers.

"Things had gotten kinda quiet when Sir John run out of far-away places to send me along with Alexander the ape and Ole Lightning the Plott Hound — then this new officer Captain Bertram came up with a notion . . ."

I'M SURE THE DEPOT COMMANDER WOULD WISH YOU TO TAKE ON SUCH AN IMPORTANT GUARD DUTY, BUT HE IS RELUCTANT TO ADD TO YOUR WORK-LOAD, COLONEL FLOOD!

THREADNEEDLE. ST.

DOGGONE IT IF THAT AIN'T PURELY LIKE SIR JOHN.

"How could your child, Zeb, know he was caught up in a flim-flam . . ."
YES, COLONEL FLOOD, AREA COMMAND HEADQUARTERS HAS BEEN NOTIFIED AND YOU MAY COMPLY WITH THE REQUISITION.

"The strongroom being locked was no problem to Major Symes and his boys . . ."
THAT REDCAP LOOKS LIKE HE'S DONE THIS BEFORE.
MP
NOT THE FIRST TIME THOSE IDIOTS AT AREA HAVE RUSHED THROUGH AN EMERGENCY WITHOUT SUPPLYING THE COMBINATION, SIR.

WOWEE! THAT SURE IS A HEAP OF MONEY.
YOU GET USED TO IT IN MY LINE OF WORK.

"The Major had me check off every last five-pound, one-pound and ten-shilling note he took out . . .
THAT IS ALL APART FROM MY SIGNING THE REQUISITION TO MAKE IT OFFICIAL.
MP

DROP IN AGAIN ANY TIME, MAJOR.
I'LL TRY, SIR — ER, DASH IT! I WAS GOING TO OFFER YOU A CIGAR, BUT I APPEAR TO HAVE MISLAID MY CASE.

"Major Symes and his Redcaps were driving off when I saw something was wrong . . ."
DOGGONE IT, ALEXANDER, NOW ME AND THE MAJOR'S FIGURING IS ALL WRONG.

"Next day it turned out I'd been hornswoggled . . ."
BANK OF ENGLAND ROBBED

"Sir John put a brave face on the sorry business . . ."
GRAVE DERELICTION OF DUTY AND POSSIBLE COLLUSION IN THE THEFT OF TWO MILLION POUNDS! AHEM, COURTMARTIAL CHARGES, FLOOD! EVEN YOUR ROYAL WARRANT WILL NOT SAVE YOU FROM BEING DRUMMED OUT OF THE REGIMENT!

"Me 'n Alexander 'n Lightning was marched off in disgrace to the cooler . . ."
'It sure looked like I had brought shame on all us Floods that ever held the Royal warrant earned by the first Zebadiah . . ."
THANK'EE, ALEXANDER, BUT I DON'T FEEL LIKE A CIGAR RIGHT NOW.

AND DON'T YOU SMOKE IT YOURSELF! DOGGONE IT, I'VE SEEN THAT STOGIE-CASE AND FLAME-THROWER SOME PLACE BEFORE.

THAT CROOKED MAJOR SYMES HAD 'EM.
COMPLIMENTS OF
T.B. HORROCKS AND CO.
133 WESTON STREET.

I RECKON YOU HAVE COME UP WITH A TRAIL, ALEXANDER — IF'N ONLY I CAN GET OUT OF HERE TO FOLLOW IT.

COUSIN, I'D BE OBLIGATED BY YOU SENDING WORD TO SARN'T-MAJOR MINCHIN THAT I NEEDS HIM IN A HURRY.

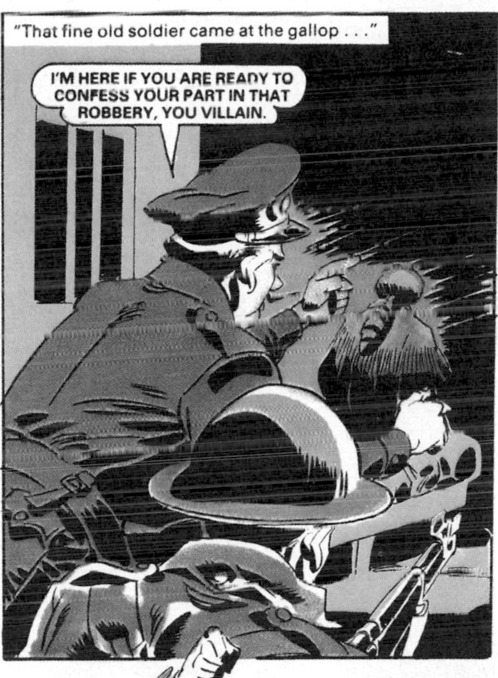
"That fine old soldier came at the gallop . . ."
I'M HERE IF YOU ARE READY TO CONFESS YOUR PART IN THAT ROBBERY, YOU VILLAIN.

SPEAK UP — HUH! THE APE!

"I dropped in on him and the guard . . .

"I sure hated what had to be done, but it was quicker than explaining . . ."
URGH — GLURK!
"We snook out of Potomac Barracks . . ."
"After that I looked for the next best critter to a mule . . ."
HEY! LOOK OUT!
WESTON STREET IF YOU PLEASE, SUH.
FLIPPING HECK — ER, YES, IT AIN'T FAR.
"The lettering showed that lighter was one given away to customers and I was hoping them Horrocks folks could give me a lead on that varmint calling himself Major Symes . . ."
"Them thar English can be terrible mistrustful . . ."
COUSIN, I SWEAR YOU WILL BE PAID IF YOU CALL IN AT POTOMAC BARRACKS.
I'VE BEEN CAUGHT LIKE THAT BEFORE, MATE. YOU HAND OVER TWO POUNDS FIVE SHILLINGS OR I'M CALLING THE POLICE.
"There's times Alexander can be real useful . . ."
THIS FIVER'LL DO JUST FINE, SIR. THANK YOU VERY MUCH, SIR.

ALEXANDER, YOU ARE GETTING SO LIGHT-FINGERED. I'M GLAD WE WASN'T GUARDING THEM ENGLISH CROWN JEWELS.
PRINTWORKS
AND CO.

"There was noise coming from the back of that building. Durned if it wasn't them two fake military cops doing a paint job on that automobile I had chased at the bank . . .
4

WE'LL ATTEND TO THEM BOYS AFTER I'VE HAD A LOOK AT WHO'S IN THAT OFFICE.

WELL, WELL, MY FRIEND CAPTAIN BERTRAM WHO GAVE ME THE NOTION OF TAKING OVER THAT BANK GUARD.

CAPTAIN, LET'S BE REASONABLE. TWO MILLION IS A LOT OF MONEY.
BUT WELL EARNED BY ME FOR SETTING UP THE JOB, OLD BOY. THINK HOW LONG IT WOULD TAKE YOU TO FORGE AS MUCH ON YOUR MACHINES.

"I walked in on those two varmints . . ."
CRIPES! IT'S HIM.
BY JOVE, SO IT IS.

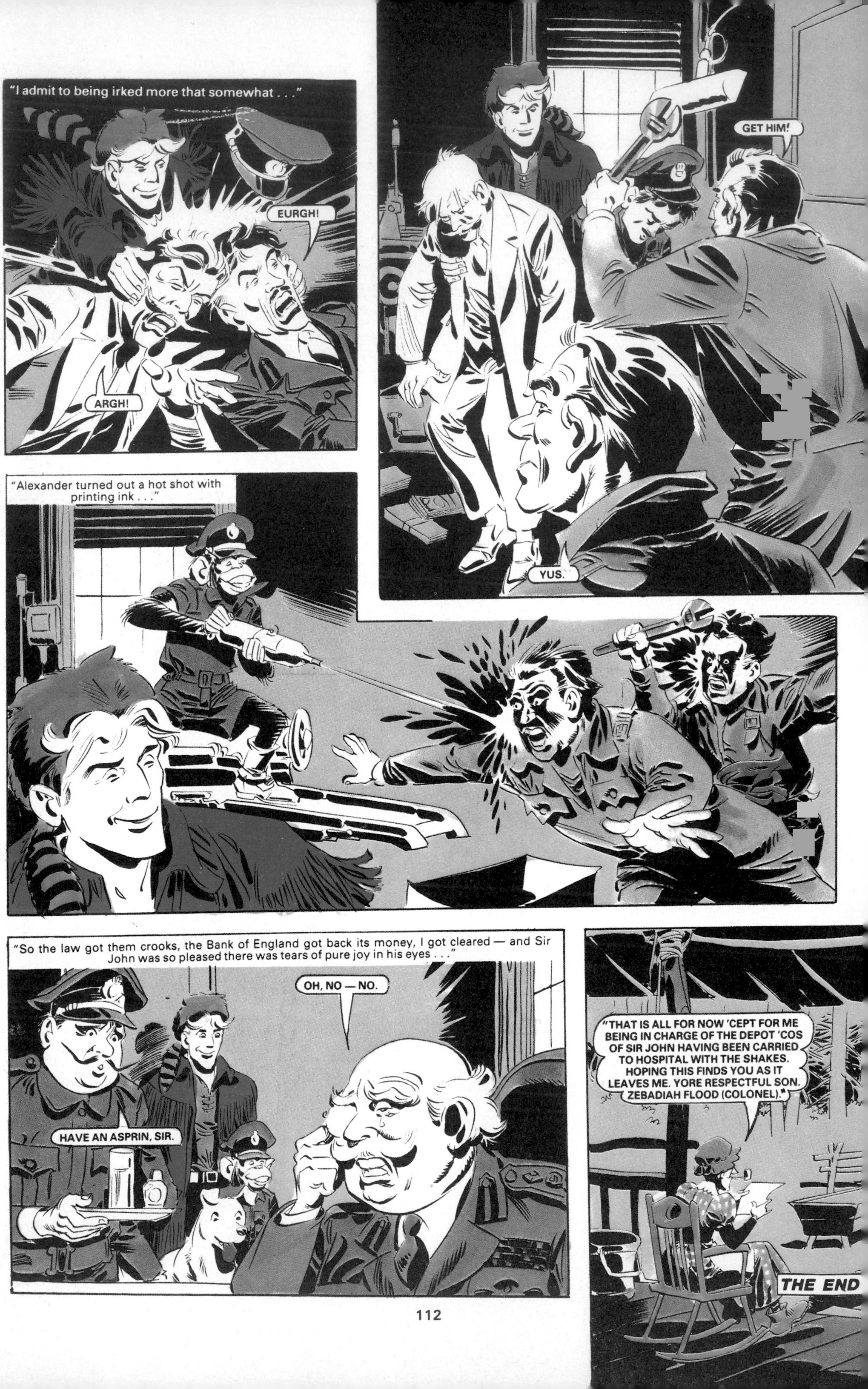

GET HIM!

YUS.

"Alexander turned out a hot shot with printing ink . . ."

CONTINUED FROM PAGE 64

SERGEANT SIXTY

Sixty took the tape home and sat down to watch it . . .

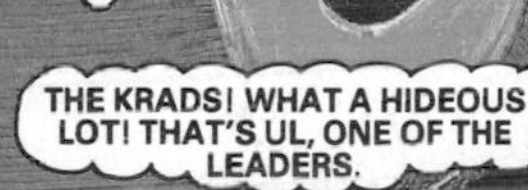

THE LAST OF THEM WERE SUPPOSED TO HAVE BEEN TRAPPED AND MASSACRED BY KING HALAT FIVE HUNDRED YEARS AGO!

IT WAS SAID THE KRADS HAD INVENTED A DIMINUNISER — A MACHINE THAT COULD KILL AND REDUCE MEN AND OBJECTS TO PUNY SIZES. KING HALAT CAPTURED IT AND TURNED IT AGAINST THEM —

THE RAVINGS OF OLD BARDS, I SUPPOSE. THAT WAS A VERY CLEVER SPOOF BATTLE.

Later . . .
SERGEANT SIXTY? A PRESENT . . .
A PRESENT? DON'T TELL ME IT'S MY BIRTHDAY.

"LEARNING OF YOUR RECENT INTEREST IN KRAD MYTHOLOGY, I THOUGHT YOU'D APPRECIATE THIS. A WELL WISHER." WELL, WHAT DO YOU KNOW. A MODEL OF A KRAD!

THE PROF'S DAUGHTER MUST HAVE MENTIONED MY INTEREST IN THE TAPE.

That night —
A SIGNAL FROM THE DIMINUNISER WILL BE PICKED UP BY THE KRAD MUMMY . . .

The Krad model began to grow — and became alive!

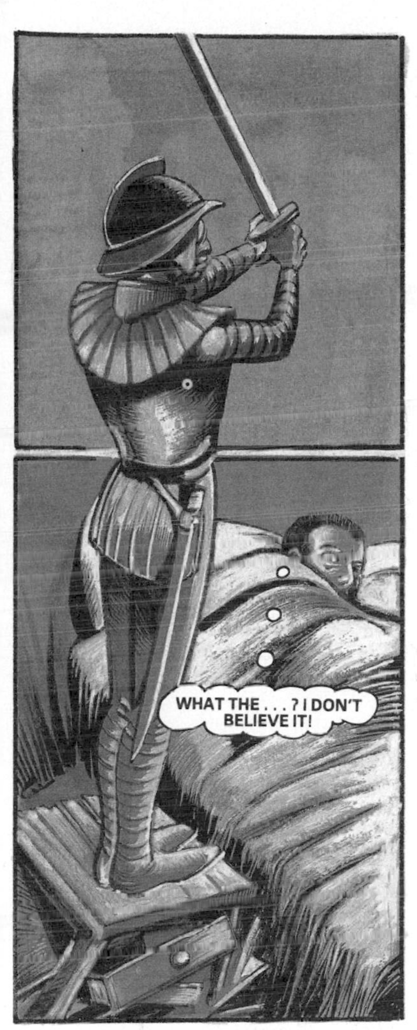

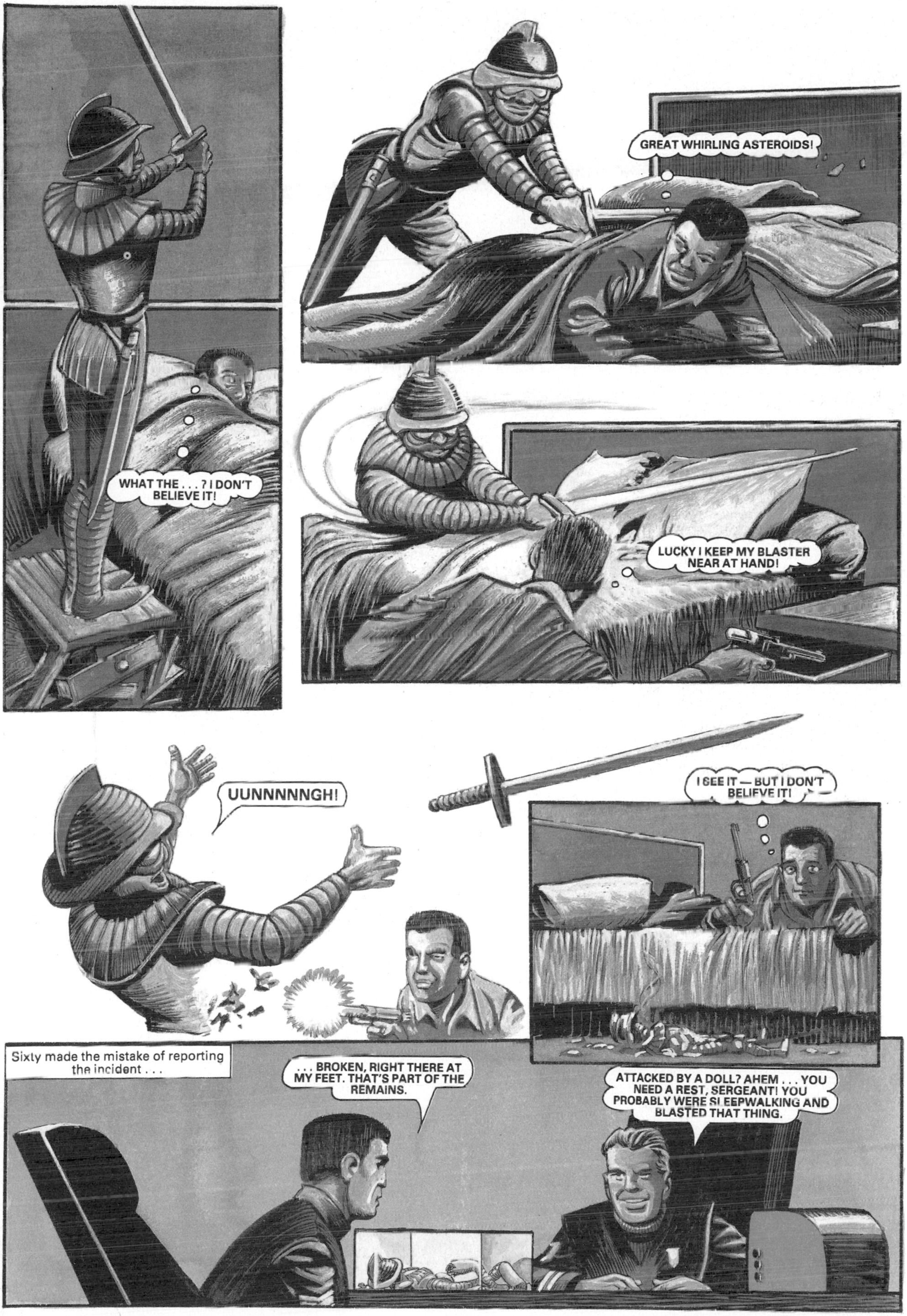

UUNNNNNGH!

I SEE IT — BUT I DON'T BELIEVE IT!

Sixty made the mistake of reporting the incident . . .

. . . BROKEN, RIGHT THERE AT MY FEET. THAT'S PART OF THE REMAINS.

ATTACKED BY A DOLL? AHEM . . . YOU NEED A REST, SERGEANT! YOU PROBABLY WERE SLEEPWALKING AND BLASTED THAT THING.

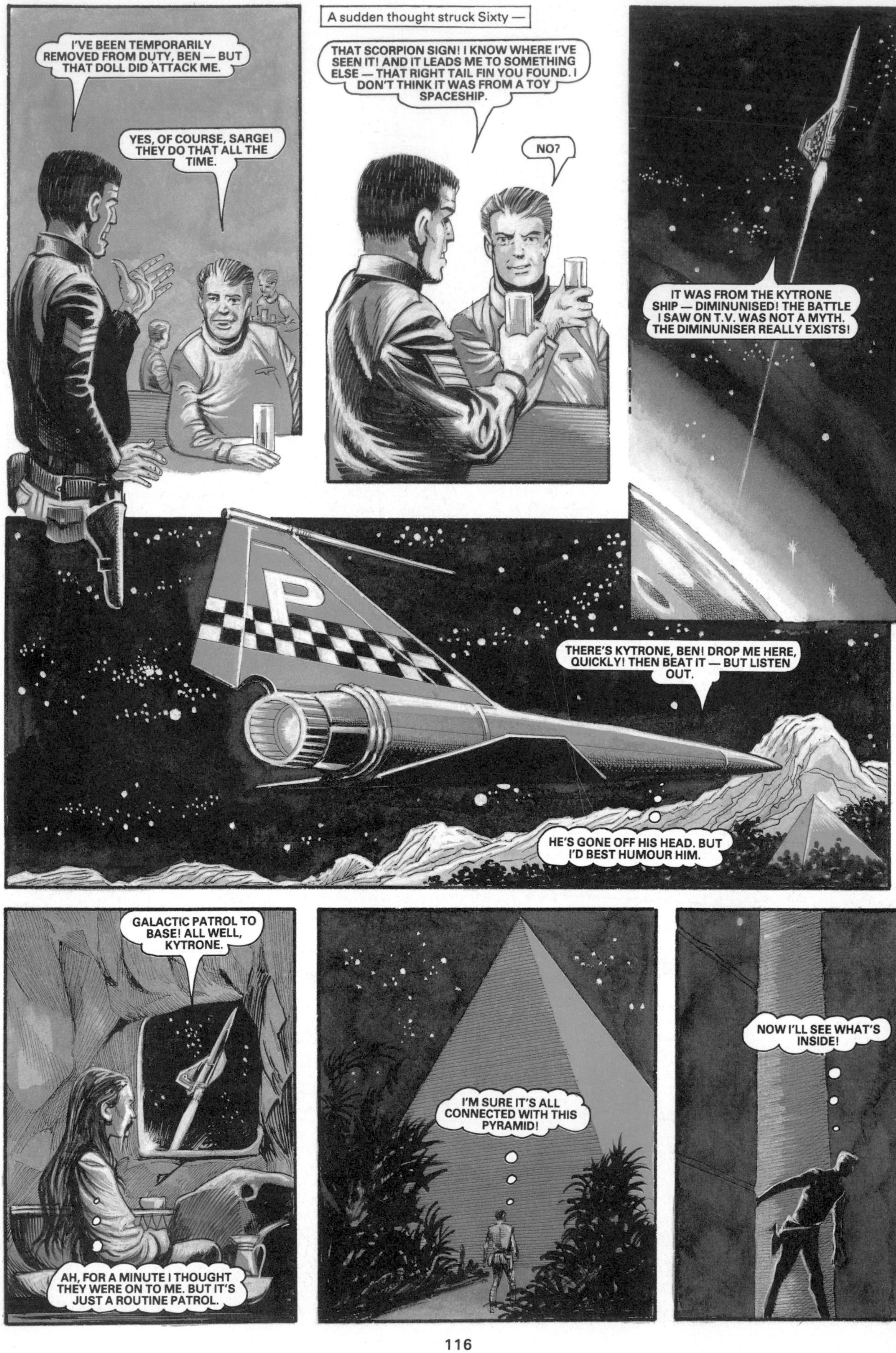

I'VE BEEN TEMPORARILY REMOVED FROM DUTY, BEN — BUT THAT DOLL DID ATTACK ME.

YES, OF COURSE, SARGE! THEY DO THAT ALL THE TIME.

A sudden thought struck Sixty —

THAT SCORPION SIGN! I KNOW WHERE I'VE SEEN IT! AND IT LEADS ME TO SOMETHING ELSE — THAT RIGHT TAIL FIN YOU FOUND. I DON'T THINK IT WAS FROM A TOY SPACESHIP.

NO?

IT WAS FROM THE KYTRONE SHIP — DIMINUNISED! THE BATTLE I SAW ON T.V. WAS NOT A MYTH. THE DIMINUNISER REALLY EXISTS!

THERE'S KYTRONE, BEN! DROP ME HERE, QUICKLY! THEN BEAT IT — BUT LISTEN OUT.

HE'S GONE OFF HIS HEAD. BUT I'D BEST HUMOUR HIM.

Sixty sent a signal from his wrist transmitter . . .

And —

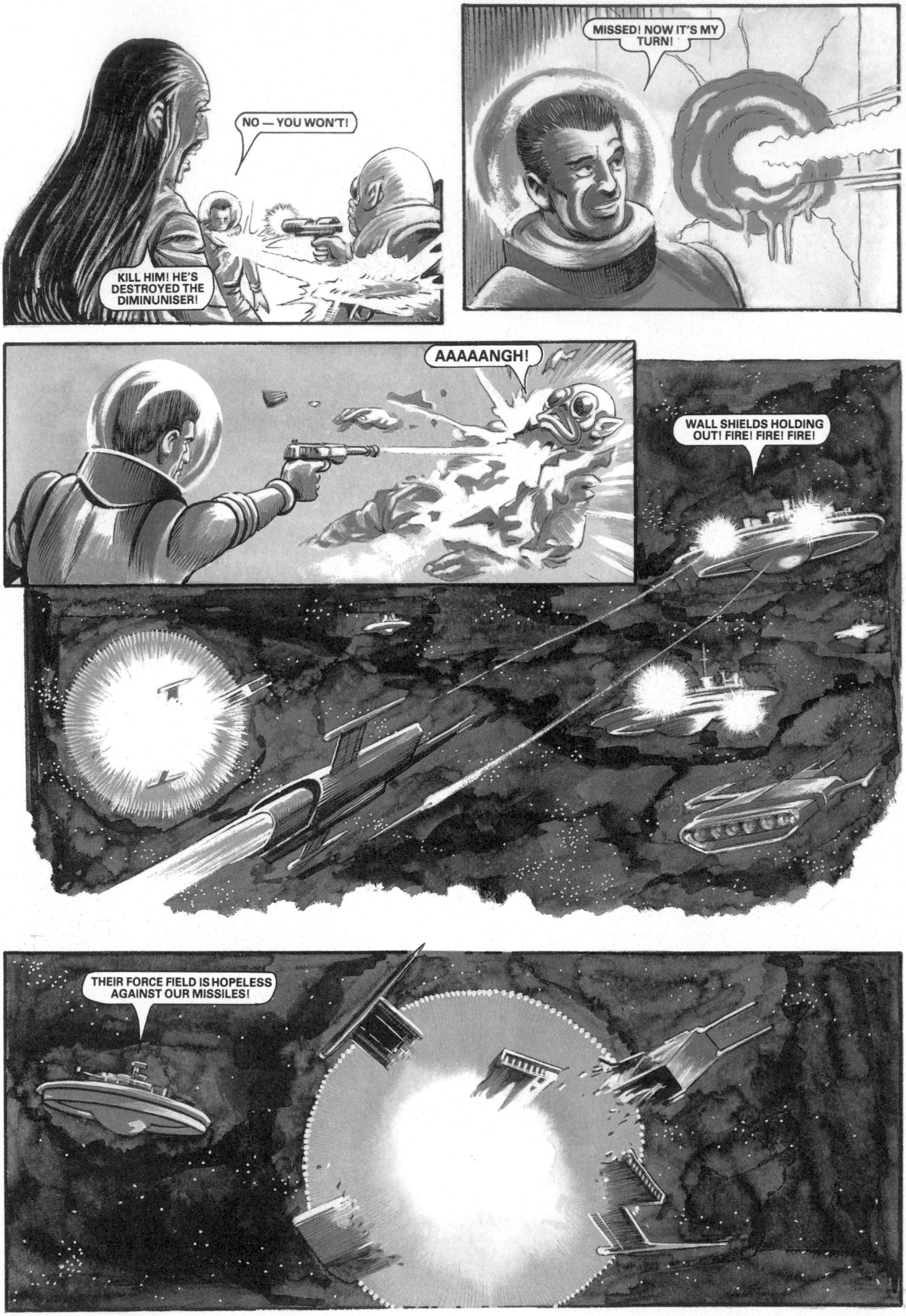

AAAAANGH!

WALL SHIELDS HOLDING OUT! FIRE! FIRE! FIRE!

THAT'S THE LAST ONE. SIXTY'S SIGNAL CAME FROM IT . . . BUT THERE WAS NO ALTERNATIVE BUT TO BLAST IT!

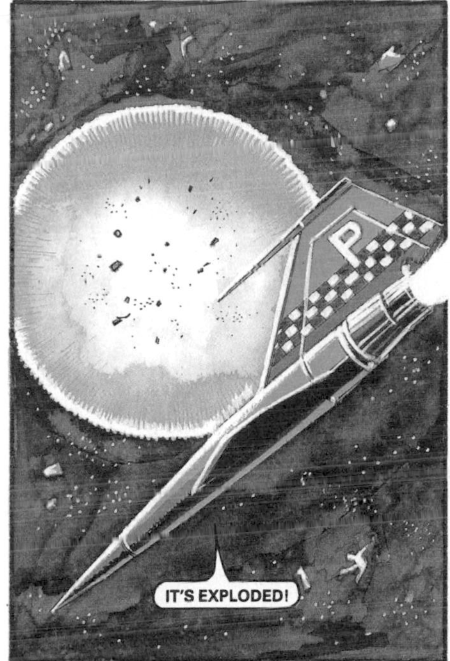
IT'S EXPLODED!

I'M OKAY! SHE'S STILL UNDER CONTROL!
WATCH THAT WRECKAGE, BEN!

Something caught Ben's eye and he went into reverse thrust — fast!
PULSATING PLANETS! IT'S SIXTY! I'D BETTER GET HIM IN FAST! THE AIR IN HIS SPACESUIT WON'T LAST FOR LONG!

GEE, I NEVER THOUGHT TO SEE YOU ALIVE! WHAT ABOUT SEZOR?
DEAD AS A DOORPOST! ALL THE KRAD WARRIORS TOO! THIS NIGHTMARE IS OVER!

INCREDIBLE, SARGE! SEZOR DIMINUNISED THE PROFESSOR'S SHIP YOU SAY, TO STOP HIM POKING AROUND.
YEH, BEN. THEN HE RESTORED IT TO NORMAL SIZE, AS IF IT HAD BEEN HIT BY A ROCK STORM! THE REAL CLINCHER WAS REMEMBERING THAT SCORPION PENDANT HE WORE . . . THE SAME SCORPION SIGN WAS DAUBED ON THE PLUNDERED FREIGHTERS.
THE END

The BIG PALOOKA
On a night in August, 1943, during the Second World War, a schooner laden with a raiding force of U.S. Rangers bore down on a Greek island garrisoned by German and Italian troops . . .
MAKE READY FIRST SHORE PARTY!
British Commando Sergeant Jim Ransom was newly attached to the American force . . .
LOOKS LIKE I LOSE AGAIN.
CALL IT AN INVESTMENT IN LEARNING THE SCIENCE OF POKER, SERGEANT RANSOM!
ATTENTION, YOU GUYS! TEX, ACE AND — ER, SERGEANT RANSOM REPORT ON DECK FOR THE SCOUT DETAIL.
LOOTENANT, THAT BIG PALOOKA IS SO DUMB IT'S KINDA SHAMING TO TAKE MONEY OFF HIM.
HUM!
Lieutenant Gard did not know what to make of the Britisher foisted on his force at the final briefing . . .
THE ITALIANS WILL HAVE HEARD OF THEIR COUNTRY'S SURRENDER AND MAY NOT PUT UP MUCH OF A SHOW. YOU CAN EXPECT THE MAIN RESISTANCE TO BE FROM JERRY. WELL, CHAPS, THAT JUST ABOUT WRAPS IT UP . . .

MAJOR MUDD, I AM LETTING YOU HAVE SERGEANT RANSOM FOR THE TRIP. HE SPEAKS A FEW LANGUAGES AND YOU MAY FIND HIM USEFUL IN OTHER WAYS.

GUYS GET DETACHED EITHER BECAUSE THEY ARE VERY GOOD OR NO GOOD AT ALL. I'M WONDERING WHAT WE HAVE IN THAT BIG PALOOKA, GARD!
MY BOYS WILL KEEP HIM IN LINE, MAJOR.

The scout detail went ashore by rubber boat . . .

ALL CLEAR! I'LL SIGNAL IN THE MAIN PARTY.
WHAT?
BEG PARDON, SIR. LISTEN!

ENGINE NOISE, SIR! ANOTHER VESSEL IS OUT THERE!

JERRY PATROL CRAFT, MAJOR MUDD. LOOKS LIKE A CASE FOR A RAPID DEPARTURE!

DOGGONE IT. THERE GOES OUR SCHOONER! THEY'RE RUNNING OUT ON US.
NO CHOICE SIR. I SUGGEST WE PICK BETTER COVER THAN THIS BEACH IN CASE THAT FIRING DRAWS A PATROL.
AT LEAST THE BIG PALOOKA SEEMS TO KNOW WHERE HE'S GOING.
SERGEANT RANSOM, APPEARS TO ME YOU HAVE BROUGHT US SLAP UP AGAINST THE MAIN GARRISON.
LOOKS THAT WAY TO ME TOO, SIR. MIGHT BE AN IDEA IF YOU BLOKES TOOK COVER HERE WHILE I NOSED AROUND.
The Americans waited and waited . . . .
THREE HOURS NOW! WHAT IN THUNDER IS KEEPING THAT BIG PALOOKA?
AHEM — ER, HERE I AM, SIR.
FACT IS — ER, I BROUGHT COMPANY! THIS IS MAJOR FABRUZZI, COMMANDER OF THE ITALIAN COMPANY HERE.
BUONA SERA.
THESE ARE SOME OF HIS BLOKES. NICE LOT — I'VE JUST BEEN HAVING COFFEE WITH THEM.
JUPITER! THE BIG PALOOKA'S SOLD US OUT.

RANSOM, WHAT IN TARNATION IS GOING ON?
JUST USING MY HEAD, SIR. CAN'T HIDE OUT FOR LONG ON AN ISLAND THIS SIZE AND I RECKON WE'LL BE BETTER OFF AS PRISONERS OF ITALIANS THAN GERMANS. NOW IF WE JUST HAND OVER OUR WEAPONS . . .
LOOK AT THE BIG PALOOKS AND THAT ITIE GETTING ALONG LIKE OLD BUDDIES.
I CAN'T FIGURE OUT IF HE'S JUST PLAIN DUMB OR THE BIGGEST RAT IN THE ARMY.
A KRAUT!
AHUH — AND LOOK AT THE FLAG ON THAT BUILDING!
THAT'LL BE THE KRAUT BARRACKS.
In the Italian quarters . . .
THE MAJOR WOULD BE MUCH OBLIGED IF YOU'D ANSWER A FEW QUESTIONS.
NAME, RANK AND NUMBER IS ALL HE'LL GET OUT OF ME AND MY BOYS — AND YOU TOO, BUSTER. THAT IS AN ORDER.
SORRY, SIR, BUT I'VE ALREADY AGREED TO TELL THE MAJOR ALL HE WANTS TO KNOW.
WHAT? WHY, YOU GOLDURNED TRAITOR! DON'T DO IT, MAN. IT'LL MEAN A COURTMARTIAL — A FIRING SQUAD!

HE'LL BE WARNING 'EM ABOUT THE RAID. THE SCHOONER'LL BE BACK TONIGHT IF THEY MANAGED TO SHAKE THAT KRAUT GUNBOAT — AND THE KRAUTS AND ITIES'LL KNOW EXACTLY WHERE AND HOW THEY'RE COMING IN.
GRUB UP, BLOKES.
KEEP YOUR FOOD, YOU TREACHEROUS RAT — AND HERE'S SOMETHING FOR AFTERS.
GO EASY, SIR! THE MAJOR'S COME TO TELL YOU THAT HE'S BEEN ORDERED TO TURN US OVER TO THE JERRIES — BUT HE WON'T DO IT. HE AND HIS MEN WISH TO COME OVER TO OUR SIDE LIKE HIS ARMY IS DOING IN ITALY.
The Rangers decided to have breakfast . . .
SERGEANT RANSOM, WHAT EXACTLY HAVE YOU BEEN TELLING THESE ITIES?
ONLY THE TRUTH, BUT I STRETCHED IT A BIT, SIR. I MADE THE RAID INTO A BIG INVASION. THE MAJOR GOT SO KEEN TO CHANGE SIDES THAT ONLY ONE THING STOPPED HIM ATTACKING JERRY RIGHT AWAY . . .
THOSE FIELD GUNS OUTSIDE THE JERRY BARRACKS! I TOLD HIM NOT TO WORRY BECAUSE WE'D TAKE CARE OF THEM.
The Rangers found themselves armed again — and following Jim!
YOU BLOKES COULD WAIT HERE WHILE I CHECK OUT THOSE GUNS — IF YOU'LL EXCUSE THE SUGGESTION, SIR.
RANSOM, RIGHT NOW I'M TOO DIZZY TO DO ANYTHING EXCEPT EXCUSE YOU.

WHERE IS THAT BIG PALOOKA? HE COULD TEACH AN APACHE TRICKS ABOUT SNEAKY MOVING.
LOOK! HE'S SNUK UP ON ONE OF THE GUNS.
SORRY, FRITZES.
URH!
ARGH!
WOULD YOU MIND LOADING IN A SHELL AND CHARGE ONCE I'VE GOT THIS GUN ON LINE?
SURE — THOUGH I'D APPRECIATE BEING TOLD WHAT'S GOING ON.
THIS TELEPHONE WILL BE LINKED WITH JERRY'S HEADQUARTERS IN THE BARRACKS, SIR. I THINK IT MIGHT BE AN IDEA TO HAVE A CHAT WITH THEM.
RANSOM, I FEEL ALMOST SORRY FOR THOSE KRAUTS.
Jim made a call . . .
HERR MAJOR, HE SAYS WE ARE SURROUNDED BY A BATTALION OF SHOCK TROOPS AND THE ITALIANS HAVE JOINED THEM.
. . . and was answered!
THAT'S THE JERRY COMMANDING OFFICER. HE SAYS HE AND HIS MEN WILL FIGHT TO THE DEATH.
SO WHAT NOW?

SO NOW WE TRY PERSUASION, SIR.
The dust settled!
I RECKON JERRY IS PERSUADED, SIR.
The Italians took the surrender.
That evening —
THE REST OF THE FORCE WILL BE HERE AT DAWN! MAJOR MUDD NEEDED SOME CONVINCING THAT FOUR OF US HAD CAPTURED THE ISLAND AND TAKEN FOUR HUNDRED PRISONERS.
YESSIR — ER, SO YOU HAVE A FULL HOUSE, ACE.
SO HAVE I — ONLY MINE HAS A PAIR ROYAL WHICH I BELIEVE BEATS YOUR PAIR.
THAT CLEANS ME OUT, YOU BIG PALOOKA. I'M GETTING THE NOTION YOU'VE PLAYED THIS GAME BEFORE.
YOU AREN'T THE FIRST YANKS I'VE SERVED WITH. THEY USED TO CALL ME BY THAT SAME NAME — BIG PALOOKA. WHAT DOES IT MEAN?
I GUESS IT MEANS WE'RE KINDA GLAD YOU'RE ON OUR SIDE IN THIS WAR.
THE END